Peacekeeper's

Daughter

PEACEKEEPER'S DAUGHTER

~

A Middle East Memoir

~

TANYA BELLEHUMEUR-ALLATT

Thistledown
Press

Thistledown Press Ltd.
P.O. Box 30105 Westview Saskatoon, SK S7L 7M6
www.thistledownpress.com

Library and Archives Canada Cataloguing in Publication
Title: Peacekeeper's daughter : a memoir / by Tanya Bellehumeur-Allatt.
Names: Bellehumeur-Allatt, Tanya, author.
Identifiers: Canadiana 20210186720 | ISBN 9781771872164 (softcover)
Subjects: LCSH: Bellehumeur-Allatt, Tanya — Childhood and youth. | LCSH: Children of military personnel — Lebanon — Biography. | LCSH: Children of military personnel — Israel — Biography. | LCSH: Children of military personnel — Canada — Biography. | LCSH: French-Canadians — Lebanon — Biography. | LCSH: French-Canadians — Israel — Biography. | LCSH: Lebanon — History — Israeli intervention, 1982–1985 — Personal narratives. | LCGFT: Autobiographies. | CGFT: Personal narratives.
Classification: LCC DS87.53 .B45 2021 | DDC 956.05/2092 — dc23

Cover design by David Drummond
Printed and bound in Canada

The following material was previously published in different form: "Carrying War" in *subTerrain*, "Surprise" in *carte blanche*, "Beirut Bombing" in *EVENT* and *Best Canadian Essays 2015*, "Witness" in *Prairie Fire*, "Taking Possession" in *The New Quarterly*, "From Damascus to Beirut" in *Prairie Fire*.

THE USES OF SORROW from Thirst by Mary Oliver, published by Beacon Press, Boston Copyright © 2004 by Mary Oliver, used herewith by permission of the Charlotte Sheedy Literary Agency, Inc.

Quotation from William Golding's *Lord of the Flies* used by permission of Faber and Faber Ltd.

CALVIN AND HOBBES © 1987 Watterson. Reprinted with permission of ANDREWS MCMEEL SYNDICATION. All rights reserved.

Thistledown Press gratefully acknowledges the financial assistance of The Canada Council for the Arts, SK Arts, and the government of Canada for its publishing program.

For Brian, for always believing.

Et pour Maman, qui n'a jamais cessé de croire.

The Uses of Sorrow

(*In my sleep I dreamed this poem*)

Someone I loved once gave me
a box full of darkness.

It took me years to understand
that this, too, was a gift.

MARY OLIVER

Contents

CARRYING WAR

~

NORTH HATLEY, QUEBEC
DECEMBER 2015

"Here," I say, "this is for you." I hand my brother a copy of *Best Canadian Essays 2015* and hold my breath as I watch him read the first few paragraphs. My piece, "Beirut Bombing," is set during the year we spent as a family in the Middle East, at the centre of a war. As he reads, I recall the muezzin's call to prayer mingled with the vibrations of shelling in the Lebanon Mountains.

"Reading your work takes me right back," Maman pipes up from behind the kitchen counter, where she's preparing the cheese platter for our Christmas brunch. "I can picture the fabric of our couch in our Beirut apartment: brown, with red stripes and little black dots on top. The brown was the same shade as the leather on the door."

"A bulletproof door as thick as a mattress," I say from the adjoining room.

Etienne looks me full in the face. "How can you remember so many details?"

"I kept a journal." My friend Claire's mother gave it to me for my twelfth birthday, a few weeks before we left Canada, in August 1982. *Write everything down*, she'd said. *One day, you'll write a book about it.* I still have that journal from 1982–83, with its pages full of round, childish script — the voice of the twelve-year-old girl whose childhood ended when the war began.

Sometimes people can't remember a thing about the events that marked them, but I remember small details from the year I was twelve, when we moved from Yellowknife, Northwest Territories, to Israel, and then Lebanon. It's as if someone pressed the pause button and a frame got stuck on the screen.

Still, for the longest time, in the mythology of my family, our year in the Middle East was my father's story. He was the hero at its centre, the reason we'd landed in Beirut at the height of the civil war. At family gatherings, whenever the story came up, he was the one to tell it. My brother Etienne, Maman, and I were secondary, supporting characters. It took me many years to realize it was my story too.

Now, my father — deaf in one ear, a firing range injury — sits quietly while the rest of us talk. "I can see it perfectly," Maman says. "Our mahogany dining room table in Beirut had a strip of mirror down the middle." She arranges devilled eggs on a china plate. "Fancy, but highly impractical. I was constantly removing smudges."

"The furniture would travel across the carpet when the shelling got bad," Etienne says. "We'd have to rearrange it in the morning, before going to school."

Etienne's twelve-year-old son looks up from his video game, then studies the living room carpet as if it holds a secret.

"Remember the envoy from the Canadian government?" Etienne imitates the man, a nervous tic jerking his face sideways. "I can still see him with his hand on the doorknob, saying 'How can you live like this?' He was practically in tears."

"He left halfway through dinner." Maman laughs. "I wanted him to stay for dessert, but he was too petrified to eat."

Etienne runs his fingers over the open book in his hand as if reading Braille. "I wish I'd kept a journal."

He's forgotten how he hated school, hated to write. It was years later, well into his twenties, that he studied journalism at Ryerson. Growing up, we were opposites. He was the athlete and the extrovert; I was the intellectual who took refuge in books.

"You sketched," I say.

I remember torn pages laid out on the dining room table. An eyeball that was also a picture of the Earth, with its continents and oceans drawn in coloured pencil behind the pupil and iris. To the side of the globe a large wound gaped open, with blood spurting off the page. Next to it, people lay on their backs, their faces distorted into screaming holes. Under them were other bodies, mangled and twisted into strange positions. Blood everywhere. Over the nightmarish scene hovered a huge pair of disembodied eyes, partly obscured by cumulus clouds.

"I told Maman to read herself as a character." I hope my voice sounds light and cheerful. "You'll need to do the same." The events I describe took place almost forty years ago. We've all changed a great deal. Perhaps we will barely recognize ourselves. But writing about people you love, telling their stories, is a high-wire act; it comes with intrinsic risks. This story is not a pretty or a happy one. I haven't made us shine. If anything, I've angled the camera in such a way that we are all cast in shadow. I needed to do it this way in order to tell my truth — what Emily Dickinson calls "telling it slant."

My brother hands me a pen. "I'd like you to autograph my copy."

I steady my hand before signing my name on the title page. I tried not to exploit his pain or fictionalize the truth. If he argues that I didn't get it right, that I mixed things up, I'm prepared to defend my point of view. Eyewitness accounts can hold vast variations — it depends on where the witness is standing.

I wonder what he'll think when he gets to the part about the bombing. The embassy man covered in white dust, holding the woman whose eyes were full of blood. The cars wrapped around telephone poles. The empty crater where the magnificent building had once stood. Sirens sounding the death toll.

"Everything's ready," my mother announces from the kitchen.

"No kid should ever see those things," my brother says in a low voice as he sits down at the table. His face is as white as the porcelain teacup my mother places before him. "Severed arms and legs, a body that was only a torso and a head."

My father shows no sign of having heard. But my brother's son stares at him before skewering a couple of meatballs with a toothpick and dipping them into the bowl of cocktail sauce. "What were you doing there?" he asks the four of us. "Why did you go?"

I have a few answers, but mostly they lead to more questions. Perhaps, I keep thinking, I'll finish telling this story, someday. I'll write down all my memories and find some kind of resolution.

"Everything's a story," wrote Frances Hodgson Burnett. "You are a story. I am a story." As a writer, I believe this is wonderfully true. And terrifying. This book is composed of all the stories I've written about that one year that changed my family — it's my story. But it's also my parents' story, and my brother's, told from my twelve-year-old point of view. I've spent years wrestling it onto the page, sifting through the memories, trying to understand what happened to us — to me — and why.

My father on the Golan Heights, October 1982.

~

LEAVING YELLOWKNIFE

~

"Tiberias is only a half-day's drive through the desert to Jerusalem." My father uncorked the bottle of Merlot and poured himself a glass, his face framed by the candles in the centre of the table. Outside our dining room windows, the arctic wind howled. The sky had been dark since two that afternoon. Low-hanging clouds and blowing snow made it hard to see beyond a few feet. For the past three years, we'd been living in Yellowknife, where my father served as a logistics officer for the Canadian Armed Forces.

"*La Terre sainte*," Maman said. "A place of wonders: Three harvests of strawberries a year. Fresh figs. Dates. Olives." We couldn't get any of those things in Yellowknife without paying a fortune.

"The UN gives lots of time off. Isolation pay. A chance at a promotion." My father filled my mother's wine glass.

"No more mukluks and parkas." Maman ran her hand through her newly permed hair. "And there will be other French-speaking families — from Europe — with kids your age." She looked ready to leave Yellowknife that minute.

Although my parents had opted to send my brother and me to English school, they insisted that we all speak French at home; if we addressed Maman in English, she wouldn't answer. Since we were the only French-speaking family in Yellowknife, she claimed it was the only way we'd keep our language and culture alive.

Etienne, my thirteen-year-old brother, loved the North. Everything about his face said *bad news*. He pushed his plate away. "Coach Michaels told me I have a good chance of making the senior football team next year."

I didn't mind leaving Yellowknife, but I dreaded saying goodbye to my best friend, Catherine. I curled the ends of my braids around my fingers. "How far away are we going?" It had taken us three weeks to drive from the Valcartier army base in Quebec to Yellowknife; we'd made it into a family vacation, with a camping trip in the Rockies along the way. For most of my twelve years, we'd been on the move.

"I'll show you," said Maman. I listened to Daddy chew his boeuf bourguignon while she left the room and came back with the enormous *Reader's Digest Family Atlas*. "We're here." She put her finger on Great Slave Lake, an easy find at the top of North America. From there, she slid her finger to the right, over the Atlantic Ocean and Europe, until it stopped on a country the size of a slivered almond. "Israel."

"Very dangerous." Etienne sounded angry, maybe because we'd ignored what he'd said about the football team. "Israel is a war zone. We talked about it in social studies. Mr. Kelso called it a hotbed."

Maman patted her curls as if to check that they were still there.

"There's been a ceasefire for the last few months." My father swished the wine around in his glass. The candlelight accentuated the ginger highlights in his moustache. "Things are quiet. We'll be able to travel into Syria and Egypt. Visit the pyramids. Greece in the springtime."

"Normal people go to Hawaii for vacation," my brother continued.

"Etienne." Maman used her *don't talk to your father that way* voice.

I liked the idea of family holidays and going to the beach. But Etienne was making me nervous. What if he was right?

He made a fist around his fork. "You promised you'd take me on a caribou hunt next winter." He threw the fork onto his plate, splattering gravy over the embroidered peach tablecloth. "You're not asking us what we think. You're just telling us what you decided." When he pushed his chair back from the table it crashed to the floor. He stomped out of the room and up the stairs.

I picked up our dinner plates and brought them to the counter while Maman pulled her apple pie out of the oven.

"You're not worried, are you?" Maman put the pie on the

table and eyed me up and down. "We don't want your ulcer coming back."

A couple of years before, I'd been hospitalized for a week in Edmonton to determine the cause of the extreme stomach aches that had plagued me for three years, causing contractions as severe as those of a woman in labour. Once cancer and other diseases had been ruled out, I'd been diagnosed with a peptic ulcer and given a six-month treatment of Tagamet to eliminate the buildup of acid each time I got nervous or excited.

"I'm okay." It was a lie. Maman's celebration dinner was souring in my stomach.

"There's nothing to worry about." My father poured the last of the wine into his glass. He had already served several six-month missions with UNTSO — the United Nations Truce Supervisory Organization — monitoring ceasefires and supervising armistice agreements in Egypt and on the Golan Heights that border Syria and Israel. "The Canadian government wouldn't open this up to families if it wasn't safe."

When I told my grade six class about our upcoming move to the Middle East, my teacher, Mrs. Nouger, looked at me as if I'd announced that my parents were getting a divorce. "Oh." She wiped her chalky hands on her navy blue maternity dress. "Why?"

Before I had a chance to explain, Leah Sheck snickered, "Your parents should have their heads examined."

"Before they get blown off," Ricky Snaggins, the boy in front of me, blurted.

After the bell rang, Mrs. Nouger called me to her desk and gave me her mailing address. "You'll have to write to me and let me know how you're doing," she said, rubbing her pregnant belly, "so I don't worry too much." I stuffed the note in my pocket, pleased by my teacher's attention, but puzzled by her concerned expression. My father had already served two UN missions in the Middle East, for six months at a time. He knew what he was doing.

When I came out for recess, Catherine had saved me the best swing, the one that made me feel as if I was sailing right over the roof of the school, as long as I kept my legs pumping fast enough.

"We're moving too." She used her mitten to push her bangs out of her gentle brown eyes. "We just found out. My dad got promoted. We're going to Petawawa."

"I lived there before kindergarten," I said.

"Maybe I'll get to live in your old house."

"Cool." I tried to remember what our Petawawa house on the army base looked like, but couldn't.

"Jump!" Catherine flew off her swing and landed on her feet, arms in the air like Nadia Comaneci at the Olympics.

I wanted to do the same, but I was worried I might land on my head or scrape the skin off my legs. I stopped pumping and let the swing lose momentum, then hopped to the snow-packed ground.

Catherine slipped her mittened hand into mine. "I'll miss you."

"Me too." My legs felt wobbly and my head was dizzy, but I didn't want Leah Sheck to see me cry.

We packed our things into two sets of boxes. "I am a packing expert," Maman declared. "I've done it ten times in eighteen years of marriage." She brandished her black marker like an artist's paintbrush.

The first set of boxes held all the things we'd purchased for the Middle East, in case we couldn't find them there: dried soup, foot powder, moustache wax, brownie mix, antibiotic cream, and disposable toilet seat covers. Alongside these were all the essentials that we couldn't live without. I packed two dozen teen novels, my pencil case, my cherrywood alto recorder, my autograph book with all my Yellowknife friends' mailing addresses handwritten next to their signatures.

In the boxes marked ONTARIO Maman packed up all the things we wouldn't need for our year abroad. Those possessions, along with our car, would go into storage.

She helped me stuff my pink bear into the largest box. "We'll see him again in a year." She wrote a number on the top, then recorded the box's contents on her clipboard. "But you probably won't want any of your old stuff when we get back."

I traced the shape of my bear inside the box. I wanted to rip him out and put him back on my bed.

By the end of the school year, four months after my father's announcement, the house was almost dismantled, like a Christmas tree stripped of its decorations. Daddy lined up his binocular collection on the dining room table.

"Why are you taking those?" Etienne had given away almost all his clothes, books, and old toys to the church rummage sale, convinced by Maman that in a year's time he would have no use for any of it. But when she'd told him that he needed to find a new home for his hamster, Mr. Schumann, he'd refused. He'd walked around with the pet in his pocket all day. While we were watching reruns of "Starsky and Hutch," Mr. Schumann had escaped.

Daddy pulled a scrapbook out of the bottom of the wicker basket at his feet. "A Photographic Guide to Birds of the Golan" was handwritten on the cover in fancy calligraphy. "I put this together in seventy-eight." He handed it to me. "Have a look."

"When do you have time for birds? What about the fighting?" Etienne's eyes narrowed and darkened. I'd heard him boast to his friends that our father was going to be part of an important military campaign in the Middle East.

"The most action I saw in the Middle East was a Druze shepherd whose flock wandered over the line into Syria," Daddy said. "It was the birds that kept us busy."

"What kind of weapons will you have out there?" Etienne asked. "Pistols? Revolvers?"

"It's against the rules," Daddy said. "Blue Berets don't carry arms."

The excitement drained from Etienne's face.

I felt more puzzled than ever. My father had shown us the headline in the *Edmonton Journal* earlier that month. On June 6, 1982 — my parents' wedding anniversary — Israeli Defense Minister Ariel Sharon launched an invasion of Southern Lebanon and laid siege to Beirut with the purpose of attacking the Palestine Liberation Organization, headed by Yasser Arafat, and forcing its withdrawal. It was the beginning of the 1982 Lebanon War.

All our neighbours and friends were still sleeping when our car pulled out of the driveway of our house on Gitzel Street. We'd said our goodbyes the night before. There were no hugs or tears like when I'd left my best friend Denise on the North Shore the summer after kindergarten, or when we'd left the Valcartier base and my best friend Claire had run after our car as far as she could. This time, there was only the spray of crushed rock under our tires and a few sniffling sounds beside me.

"Blow your nose." Daddy lit a cigarette, even though the windows were rolled up to keep the mosquitoes out.

"I don't want to go." Etienne had his hand on the door as if he planned to jump out. "I need to find Mr. Schumann."

My father turned the Ford onto Catherine's street. In a few seconds, our house would be out of view. "Soldiers don't cry." Cigarette ash fell onto the steering wheel.

"The next people who move in will find Mr. Schumann," Maman said. "He's probably nesting in the basement."

"They might think he's a mouse," I said, "and lay a trap."

Maman shushed me. "Nonsense."

"Let me go back and look for him one last time." Etienne snorted in an effort to stop the tears.

"We have a plane to catch," my father said. "We can't turn around."

My brother pulled his T-shirt over his face. *Save Energy. Fart in a Jar.* The slogan crumpled as he wiped his nose on the inside of his shirt, then tugged it down and closed his eyes. I hated to see him look so defeated.

"I left for boarding school when I was just twelve, and only went home for the summer," Daddy said as he stepped on the gas. "My father lied about my age so he could take me to the logging camps."

"He shouldn't have done that," Maman said.

"I had to work to pay my tuition."

"Stop being so hard on us," Maman whispered. "It's never easy to leave."

"I don't want my son to be *un bébé la la.*"

"I'm not a baby," Etienne mumbled.

"From the Arctic to the Middle East," Maman said in the cheerful voice she used with her students at the Yellowknife Playschool. "On to the next adventure."

I waved goodbye to all the familiar buildings: Mildred Hall Elementary School and the library, the United Church where we met for Girl Guides. We were almost at the end of Main Street. "Do you think we'll ever come back here? To live? Or even to visit?"

Daddy took a long drag on his cigarette. "I doubt it."

My mother, Etienne, and I spent the rest of the summer in Montreal with our grandparents while my father went ahead of us to begin his mission in Israel. In August, I took a bus to Ottawa to spend a week with Claire. Her family had moved there from Valcartier soon after we'd moved to Yellowknife. We fell into each other's arms, filling the gap of our three-year separation in minutes. For a week, we were inseparable. At the bus station, before I boarded for Montreal, Claire's mum gave me a blank journal wrapped in shiny paper. "Write everything down," she said, "all the details. One day, it'll be a book."

I promised I would.

From my seat on the bus, I waved goodbye one last time, through a haze of tears and diesel fumes, willing myself to memorize Claire's face.

The morning of our departure for Tel Aviv, Grandmaman hid her face in her apron. The legs of her rocker moved steadily back and forth.

I knelt beside the chair and placed my hand on her knee. "Will you visit us?"

"*Oui*," she said.

"*Non*," Grandpapa said at the same time.

Maman looked up from the newspaper she'd been reading. "But you've always visited us." I had pictures of me as a baby in a lacy baptismal gown cradled in Grandmaman's arms outside my first home in Germany.

Grandpapa got up and rinsed his cup at the sink. "What about the crisis with Syria and Lebanon? The PLO?"

Not this again.

When Maman rubbed her forehead, her fingers left an inky smudge between her eyes.

"Israel is volatile." Grandpapa dried his cup, but instead of putting it in the cupboard, he went to the stove and poured himself more coffee. "It's great to go on adventures, but don't you think this is taking it a bit far?"

"*Et les enfants.*" Grandmaman squeezed my hand. "What about them? Think of the danger."

I put my head in Grandmaman's soft lap. Her damp apron felt cool against my cheek. But her next words were a punch to my stomach.

"We think you're making a big mistake."

"How can you do this to me?" Maman pushed herself up from the table. "We fly out tonight. Donald is already there. We can't back out now."

Grandpapa took a loud slurp of his coffee. Steam from the cup blurred his glasses. "You don't need to go."

"He's my husband." Maman piled the newspaper pages haphazardly instead of the usual way, organized in sections and folded down the crease. "I need you to support my decision."

"*Au moins, laisse-nous les enfants ...*" Grandmaman put a protective hand over my head. All the air drained out of my lungs, like the empty birthday balloon on the floor near the rocker, left over from my party a few days before. Would Maman leave us behind?

"The kids need new jeans. Etienne needs a watch." Maman knocked loudly on the bedroom door off the kitchen. "Get up!"

My brother stumbled into the kitchen, bleary-eyed. "Why is everyone shouting?" he asked. "I thought I could sleep in today."

"We're going shopping," Maman said.

"But I haven't had breakfast yet."

Maman grabbed her purse from its hook in the hallway. "Take a piece of bread. Wash your face. We're going."

On the plane that night, the new jeans dug into my waist. I wished I'd taken the time to try on a few more pairs.

"We're off," Maman said, as the plane lifted. She was reading *Fodor's Guide to Israel and the Holy Land*, and marked a line on the page with a yellow highlighter. "Adjust your watches to the new time. Israel is seven hours ahead."

I fiddled with my watch buttons, but couldn't figure out how to set it.

"Check this out." Etienne pointed to the airline magazine with his chin. "It says here that El Al is the most secure airline in the world." He slid his finger along the sentence as he read. "No terrorist attacks, ever."

"What's a terrorist?" I asked.

"*Ne t'en fais pas*," my mother crooned, not looking up from her book. "Go to sleep. When you wake up, we'll be in Israel. You're going to love it."

On September 14, 1982, two and a half weeks after our arrival at Tel Aviv's Ben Gurion Airport with our dozen suitcases, boxes of books, and brand new roller skates, the newly elected president of Lebanon and supreme commander of the Lebanese Forces, Bachir Gemayel, was assassinated at his headquarters in Beirut. Israel reoccupied the western part of the city. While we were still settling into our apartment in Tiberias, terrorists stormed the Israeli-occupied Sabra and Shatila refugee camps and massacred thousands of Palestinian men, women, and children.

We had no idea how these events would impact our lives and change them forever. But we would soon find out.

Etienne, me, and Maman and our Peugeot outside Tiberias, Israel,
October 1982.

~

HEAVEN'S GATE

~

We must go on, because we can't turn back.

ROBERT LOUIS STEVENSON
TREASURE ISLAND

My first night in Israel, in the American Colony Hotel in Jerusalem's Muslim Quarter, I counted into the tens of thousands to the smooth rhythm of my brother's breathing. Wide-eyed under stiffly starched sheets, I tried to read. I'd spent the summer in Quebec ignoring reality by hiding inside a book. But that night, it wasn't refuge enough. Outside the open window, in the jungle-like garden of the hotel's inner court, two cats yelped and howled in the pleasure-pain of their heat. My body was stiff with fear.

I opened the blank journal Claire's mum had given me. At the top of the first page, I wrote the date: *August 27, 1982,* and beneath that, in capital letters that spilled into the margins, *I want to go home.*

At three o'clock, a man's voice, singing into a loudspeaker, pierced the cats' howls, and I cried out, "Maman!" but she was in another room with my father and didn't hear. I'd wanted to share a room with her instead of Etienne, but my parents had been apart all summer, since we'd left the Northwest Territories. My mother insisted that they be together now.

Once daylight came, I drifted into an exhausted sleep that ended too soon. My mother shook me awake. It was time to meet for breakfast in the hotel courtyard.

The smell of roasted coffee beans mixed with the damp green smell of the garden. My father pushed the toast rack toward me. "Eat." But I couldn't. My stomach was a mess from the heat.

"We'll visit the mosque today," he said. "The Dome of the Rock. *Qubbat as-Sakhrah.*" He looked around the table to see if we were impressed by his knowledge of the Arabic name.

"The place with the huge yellow roof?" Etienne asked.

My father nodded. "Golden, to represent holiness."

All I wanted was to get to our apartment in Tiberias. See if there were any other twelve-year-old girls in our new neighbourhood. Settle into my room. But my father insisted on giving us a tour of Jerusalem — the Holy City, he called it — so we could get acclimatized.

After a short walk through East Jerusalem, we stepped inside the massive octagonal building at its centre.

"Take off your shoes," my father instructed. Etienne scowled but did as he was told.

"Cover your head." My mother handed me a scarf that she'd pulled from her handbag.

Once shrouded, I felt like a different person. My blonde braids no longer set me apart. Since landing in Tel Aviv, I'd longed to exchange the fair hair and complexion I'd inherited from my father for my mother's and brother's dark, tanned skin that could let them pass for Israelis.

"Women here, men there," my father said.

Etienne grinned. "Our section is bigger."

"Shut up," I mumbled, and followed my mother.

"We'll meet at the Foundation Stone." My father seemed to know his way around.

The palatial mosque was full of artifacts, rich carpets, and elaborate candelabra. "Like a castle for God," my mother said in a breathless voice. Men and women knelt, prayed, and chanted while we walked around them and watched.

My father gestured to us to join him by the massive boulder, the centrepiece of the building. "This rock is the foundation stone of the entire world," he said. "The Jews believe it was from this rock that the earth was created. The Muslims believe it was on this same rock that Mohammed ascended to Heaven on his horse." He pointed to indentations in the stone. "Those are the hoof marks."

"Yeah, right," Etienne said under his breath. My mother put a hand on his arm and glared at him.

"That's why they call it the Dome of the Rock, then?" I asked.

"Yes," said a man standing nearby. His outfit was similar to my father's: short-sleeved button-down shirt tucked in at the waist, leather belt, long cotton pants with a crease down the middle, lace-up brown leather shoes.

"I am Akram." The man stepped closer to us and placed a hand on his heart. "My name means 'most generous.'" His English was good. He even sounded a bit Canadian, the way he said certain words. "I was born here. May I have the honour of giving you a tour of the lower floor?"

"Yes," said my mother.

"No," said my father.

There was a pause while the rest of us waited to see who would win.

"Very well." My father nodded to Akram.

I was surprised. My father was usually the one to decide things. He had firm opinions and did not easily change his mind. But after being away from Maman for so long, he seemed eager to please her, and to impress us all with the marvels of this ancient country that would be our home for the next six months, until the United Nations posted us to our next Middle Eastern destination.

Akram guided us into another room. "Many people believe that under this cave is a secret chamber called the Well of Souls. When you knock on the cave floor, you will hear a hollow echo." The ceiling above the narrow stone staircase was so low he had to bend his head.

My father and brother followed him into the tunnel-like entrance.

"I don't want to go down there," I whispered to Maman in French. "*J'ai peur.*"

She grabbed my hand. "You can't stay up here alone."

I felt claustrophobic on the stairs and in the small, barely lit enclosure. I craved fresh air and the wide open space of the prayer sanctuary. When Etienne knocked on the cave floor, I bolted back up the steps. The last thing I wanted was to awaken ancient ghosts who might trail behind us.

Once we were reassembled, Akram led us into the expansive walled courtyard outside the mosque. "Now I will take you on a tour of the Old City," he said. "All four quarters. Up on the walls. New places. Guaranteed."

"How much?" my father asked.

"I'm hungry," Etienne said.

"Me, too," I said. "It must be close to lunchtime."

My mother gave us one of her looks. "Not really. You're jetlagged."

"Who cares?" Etienne said. "It's lunchtime somewhere in Canada."

Akram smiled. "Follow me. I'll take care of everything."

"How much?" my father asked again. He wasn't moving, so neither were we.

"For four people," Akram said, "one hundred shekels."

"Fifty." My father fiddled with his watch.

"Seventy-five."

"All right. But first we need some food. For my son."

What about me? I felt invisible.

"Of course," Akram said. "Pita and hummus. Falafel. Dates like you've never tasted."

When we followed him out the gate, my mother slipped the scarf off her head and knotted it around her neck, the way she wore it at home. But I kept mine fastened over my hair in an effort to blend in.

We walked through a rabbit warren of cobblestone streets with kiosks and small shops selling spices, fruit, crockery, and clothing. Some shopfronts displayed brightly coloured scarves and T-shirts, embroidered tops, and leather sandals. Other kiosks sold long dresses in sober colours with matching dark headscarves, the kind I'd seen most of the women wearing at the mosque. I reached out to feel the thick fabric and wondered what it would be like to have only my eyes showing. It would be hot in there. And I'd soon get tired of all that black, brown, and grey. But the thought of a complete disguise, head to toe, appealed to me.

"This is the Via Dolorosa." Akram pointed to a small sign on the wall next to a café filled uniquely with men. They were seated at tables where they smoked long, curled pipes. I wanted to ask about them, what they were smoking, and where all the women were, but Akram was still talking.

"This is the path your Christ walked with his cross."

Etienne led out a loud sigh. "I want to go back to the hotel. This is boring."

"I thought this was the Muslim part of the city," I said, confused. "What does it have to do with Jesus?"

Akram didn't answer, even though he was next to me, close enough to hear my question.

My mother's hand went to her hip. She made eyes at my father, but he wasn't paying attention either, and was now walking beside Akram. "I hate being ignored," she said to me in French.

I shrugged. I was used to it.

The men stopped to look at a Christmas manger scene, giving us time to catch up.

"The Holy Family." My mother turned one of the pieces over in her hand. "We need to take this back to Canada."

My father offered a few shekels to the shopkeeper, then gave me the small sculpture of Mary and Joseph holding the baby Jesus. The three figures were carved out of a single piece of marbled olive wood.

I mumbled my thanks and slipped it into my pocket, unsure why I'd been chosen to receive this gift, but pleased by my father's attention. I envied the child in the centre of the sculpture, cradled by both his parents. Mary embraced the baby, while Joseph's arms encircled them both.

"Let's go." Etienne tugged on Maman's purse.

The alley dividing the shops was filling with people. Suddenly, we were shoulder to shoulder. I'd never experienced such an extreme press of people before. The temperature tripled. We stepped into the nearest shop, next to the floor-to-ceiling shelves of souvenirs, to escape the crowd.

In the street walked a group of people all dressed in white, wearing hooded shrouds tied at the waist with rope. The one at the front held a shepherd's staff. Those behind him carried a huge wooden cross above their heads. They reminded me of French-Canadian loggers transporting massive tree trunks out of the forest.

They made their way slowly forward through the crowded street. "Look," said Etienne, who stood beside me. "Those freaks are barefoot." He pointed to the end of the procession, where other white-clad men followed the huge cross on their knees. Every now and then they'd stop to kiss the cobblestones.

"Jesus, Son of David, have mercy on us," someone said many times in English. I searched for the source of the voice and found a man at the edge of the crowd, close to the storefront, walking on his knees. His face was peaceful, his eyes half-closed, but occasionally he would wince as if his kneecap had made contact with a small stone. The prayer beads in his hands looked the same as the rosary Grandmaman kept in her apron pocket. She would finger it and offer a prayer to the Virgin — *la Vierge*, as she called her — at every opportunity.

"Pilgrims," was all Akram said, once our family got back onto the street. "This route leads to the Church of the Holy Sepulchre."

If I'd been younger, still a little girl, I would have reached out to take my mother's hand. I would have leaned into her arm, felt her purse bump up against me, both child and purse like extensions of her body. But my parents walked together, behind Akram, who led the way. They didn't touch each other — my father never made any demonstrations of affection in public — but they were clearly a couple. The street wasn't wide enough for three to walk together. I fell in step beside my brother.

My senses were heightened by the extravagant displays of faith, the strange languages, the intense heat and smells: roasting coffee, spices, oranges, dust. Even my skin felt different.

We had lunch at a small café owned by Akram's cousin. Akram introduced my father to him as his Canadian friend. I wondered about that later, and whether my father had suspected, in that moment, that there was anything to fear.

"My wife and I love Jerusalem," my father said as he dipped a piece of pita into the creamy hummus. "We've been several times. Now we've brought our kids."

I wanted to love it too, for his sake. Seeing him again, in a strange place, after so many months apart, my father felt like a stranger I was getting to know. I wanted to please him, to make him proud. But I couldn't even eat the lunch; my stomach was too queasy.

We stepped out of the market into the blazing sun. I was thirsty, but we hadn't brought any water. We walked a long time. My feet burned inside my sneakers. Twice I had to ask if we could sit down. Akram showed us view after view of the city. David's Gate. Dung Gate. Jaffa Gate.

We stopped for Turkish coffee, and my father bought an English translation of the Qur'an in paperback.

"Allah will bless you," Akram said, and kissed the book on its cover before handing it to my father.

"*J'ai mal à la tête*," I whispered to my mother.

"I'm not sure where we are," she said. "We must be almost done the tour." She took the book from my father and stuffed it in her purse, then pulled out a few coins. "I'll get you some bottled water."

My headache was raging. I felt like I could have curled up and gone to sleep under the table, like a dog, except it was too hot.

The throng of people thinned the further we walked, until we had the streets to ourselves. We followed Akram up several flights of stone steps to a landing that offered a panoramic view all the way to Bethlehem in the south.

"This must be a little-known spot," my father said. "I've never been here before." He and Akram stood side by side overlooking the city: one with dark skin, hair, and eyes, the other red-headed, freckled, and fair-skinned. Akram's body was leaner and more muscular. He was taller than my father, with narrower hips. Daddy's round belly ballooned over his belt buckle. Both men had rings of perspiration under their armpits.

We were all admiring the view when Akram pulled out a knife.

It was a dagger, with a blade the length of my hand. It caught the sun and glistened. I had a vivid memory of trying to make paper catch fire on the sidewalk by angling a small mirror toward the sun. This blade would have done just as well — so shiny its owner must have kept it polished.

"Give me five hundred shekels or I call my cousins." Akram held the knife against my father's chest, pressing its point on a button of his shirt.

Both men were breathing hard. Akram's hand trembled. His fingers tightened around the knife hilt until his knuckles turned white from the pressure.

"Where are we, Akram?" my father said in a calm voice. "Remember, we're friends."

My mother grabbed my hand and crushed my fingers in a tight squeeze. The diamond from her wedding ring cut into my skin. "*Mon Dieu,*" she whispered. "*Mon Dieu.*"

"Pay up, American daddy," Akram said. With his free hand, he frisked my father's pants pockets.

The sun beat down on us. My scalp burned where I'd parted my hair earlier that morning. The tips of my ears felt hot. The scarf must have fallen down around my shoulders while we were walking. My eyes were dry, and I was dizzy. I looked around, but we were alone. Even if I cried out, there would be no one to help us.

"*Fais quelque chose*," my mother whispered. Do something.

But my father ignored her. He reached up, took hold of the man's wrist, and guided the hand holding the knife down and across his body.

Etienne stared at the knife, a fascinated look in his eyes.

"I will gladly pay you to take my family back to the city centre, where we can find our bearings again," my father said. "Thank you for this unforgettable tour of Jerusalem." He reached into the chest pocket of his shirt and pulled out a wad of bills.

When Akram accepted them with outstretched palm, my mother exhaled loudly.

My father removed the small Canadian flag he had pinned to his shirt collar and gave it to Akram. "A peace offering," he said, "to remember us by."

Akram pocketed knife, bills, and pin, turned on his heel, and led us back the way we'd come, down the hundred steps and through the maze of winding alleyways.

I tried to concentrate on the back of his head. I'd never seen anyone challenge my father, let alone threaten to harm him. My dad was a major, a high-ranking officer in the

Canadian Armed Forces. He was used to giving orders and having others obey.

"*Maman, j'ai peur*," I said.

"*Moi aussi*. But your father knows what to do."

"Good thing," Etienne mumbled. "Since he doesn't have a weapon."

My mother started to limp. She had a shrivelled calf muscle — a result of her teenage battle with polio — and her limp became more pronounced whenever she was tired or stressed.

"Thank you for finding the shop for us," my father said to Akram, once we'd reached the store that sold the wooden sculptures. He stood close to my brother, but more than six feet away from Akram. My mother and I tucked in behind my father.

"I know my city," Akram said. "This ends your tour."

"*Shukraan*." My father extended his hand.

The other man came forward and grasped it. "You are welcome."

Once Akram had left, Etienne asked, "How could you shake his hand like that? After he pulled a knife on you?"

"I didn't come here to make enemies," my father answered.

"I can't believe what he did to us," I said.

But if my father was still intimidated, he didn't show it. "We need to remember where we are," he said. "This nation has been at war for the last thirty-four years, since the day it was formed. We'll have to be more careful."

"Are you blaming me?" My mother's voice rose, and her shoulders stiffened, ready for a fight. But my father lit a cigarette.

"I want to show you the Western Wall." Smoke blurred the outline of his face. "It's a must."

"The children are tired," my mother said. "Let's go back to the hotel."

"But we only have this one day in the city," he said. "And we're right on the edge of the Jewish Quarter. The Wall is only a few minutes away."

"More walls?" Etienne groaned. "I'd like to get myself a knife like Akram's."

"It would get confiscated in the security check we have to pass through," my father said. "I'll get you some ice cream instead."

I was standing near the guarded fence outside the Western Wall, trying to stop the ice cream from melting over my hand, when I saw the first soldier. He had wrapped a white-and-blue shawl around his head and torso. His army fatigues and submachine gun stuck out the bottom. Completing the outfit was a pair of combat boots, polished to a shine. The soldier's lips moved as if he were reciting something, though no sound came out. His cheeks were wet.

My mother rifled through her handbag and produced a small notebook. "Write your prayer down." She ripped out a page and handed it to me, then did the same for my father and brother.

"What?" Etienne asked.

"It can be anything." Maman gave me a pen. "You go first."

I stared at the torn paper. The only prayer I knew was the Our Father, but it wouldn't fit on the tiny page.

"Hurry up," my father said. "We only have one pen."

I cupped my hand around the paper and wrote sos in large capital letters. If God was watching, He would understand.

"Now what?"

"Fold it as small as you can, so that it fits into a crack in the wall," Maman said.

Like at the mosque, there was a small section for the women and a much larger one for the men. I stood behind my mother in line while we waited to gain access to the wall. Around me, women sat on folding chairs. Many had brought small children and infants with them. Some read from prayer books, some sang, and some just stood and waited, like me. When our turn came, I stood beside my mother and wedged my paper into a crack in the wall, on top of many other squished messages.

I thought about kissing the stone, like the woman on my right did, but Maman was already gone. I backed away, my hand cupped around the smooth, cool olive wood of the sculpture in my pocket, then turned to join my family outside the gate.

"Time to head to Tiberias," my father said.

At last. I couldn't wait to get in the car and go to our new home.

"Will we come back here?" Etienne asked. "So I can shop for a knife?"

"Of course we'll be back," my mother said. "Tiberias is only a few hours' drive from Jerusalem. We can come every weekend if we want."

But my father shook his head. "I've been working six days a week since I got here. I have to head back to my observation post in the morning. I won't even be able to help you unpack."

A red stain spread over Maman's cheeks. "You said you'd have lots of time off."

"I can take you to Bethlehem later on today," my father said. "It's nearby."

"What about all our plans?" Maman asked. "Eilat. Cairo. Damascus. You promised."

"Everything's changed since the invasion. We've sent so many peacekeepers to Beirut, there aren't enough of us left back here."

My mother studied the Hebrew lettering on a nearby pomegranate stand as if she were able to decipher it.

"How long will that last?" I asked. We'd only just gotten Daddy back and he was leaving again.

"Not long. *Inshallah*." My father laughed as if he'd told a joke.

"What does that mean?" I asked.

Maman folded her arms across her chest. "If God wills," she said. "It's Arabic."

"What does God have to do with it?" Etienne crumpled the blue-and-white cloth cap he'd had to wear to touch the Wailing Wall.

"In the Middle East, God is part of everything." She still hadn't looked at my father.

"Great," Etienne said.

My father took a long drag on his cigarette. "Both sides of the war claim they've got God on their side."

My mother stepped away from us, toward the pomegranate seller, who was beckoning her over with his hand.

The War. The War. The War. It beat against my temples like a pulse.

"*Inshallah*," I said softly, sampling the new word on my tongue like salted cumin. But if my parents heard me, they gave no sign.

~

RISK

~

"Hope" is the thing with feathers.

EMILY DICKINSON

"Happy birthday, Etienne," my mother announced from the kitchen. "I'm making you a cake." It was the morning of September 27. We'd been in Tiberias for several weeks, but in spite of Maman's efforts, I was still struggling to think of the apartment as home. In Yellowknife, we'd lived in a four-bedroom, two-storey house with a large backyard. But now we were in a tiny furnished apartment, the only non-Israeli family in our seven-storey building on a sloping hillside in Tiberias's Orthodox quarter. Except for the stuff we'd brought with us from Canada, everything around us was foreign: language, food, music, smells, weather. We had yet to make any friends in our building or neighbourhood.

"Presents?" Etienne looked around the living room, then wandered into the kitchen, scanning the countertop and table. Maman smoothed her hand over the recipe book open on the counter. "I haven't had a chance to get you anything," she said without looking up. "I thought maybe once Daddy gets back from the Golan. What would you like?"

With a half sigh, half grunt, Etienne took a strawberry from the colander in the sink. "I want to go home."

Maman broke an egg into a bowl. "Which one of you ate peanuts in the night and left the shells all over the couch?" She'd become an expert at changing the subject whenever we talked about going back to Canada.

I was surprised to see a pile of peanut shells on the middle pillow of the large velour sofa, with its intricately carved ebony frame. "I didn't do it."

"Neither did I," said Etienne.

"Put the shells in the garbage next time." Maman handed me a plastic dustpan and a small brush.

I huffed at the injustice of it. The shells stuck to the pink velour, and I had to scrub to loosen them. With Daddy away on a peacekeeping mission on the Golan Heights for the week, I knew it had to be my brother who'd made the mess. But he was looking innocent, one hand stuffed in his pocket, the other reaching for the strawberries. I slid the peanut shells into the garbage. It was cheeky and mean of him to lie and cast the blame on me. But since it was his birthday, I decided not to press the point.

"What's with these berries?" Red juice trickled from Etienne's lower lip down to his chin. "They taste like soap."

"I had to soak them in disinfectant," Maman explained. "To get rid of the germs."

Etienne's face scrunched up with disapproval.

"They use questionable fertilizers here. I don't want you to get sick." My mother picked up a spatula, held a mixing bowl against her hip, and whipped the contents with violent energy.

In Yellowknife, strawberries were a rare treat. We'd planted some in our backyard garden, but our growing season was too short. They'd all remained green, or gone brown and spotty.

I grabbed the cornflakes box and a bowl. My hand hovered over the biggest strawberries in the colander. They were gorgeous.

"Have some," Maman said. "They're full of vitamins."

"But they taste like crap," my brother said.

My mother put down her spatula and shot him a look. "I guess I won't put any on your cake."

I had been going to the market with her every couple of days. I knew how much energy and time were required to find and then buy the food our family liked to eat. We didn't speak Hebrew; we were just learning our numbers. It was complicated.

I cut two big strawberries into pieces to add to my cereal. "Why is it so quiet outside?" No women chatting as they beat their carpets or hung their laundry over their balconies. No children playing. No car sounds in the streets.

"It's Yom Kippur," my mother said. "The Day of Atonement."

"The day of what?"

"A special day for Jewish people. A holiday." She pushed the hair back from her forehead.

"I'm going up to the Herreras'," Etienne said. "To see Roberto."

"I want to go too." Both my brother's new friends — Roberto from Argentina and Johan from Sweden — were good-looking boys. I wanted them to notice me. "I could hang out with Immaculata." Roberto's sister was older than all of us, but I'd met her when we went up to the UN headquarters, called the Tiberias MAC House — short for Mixed Armistice Commissions and located on the ceasefire lines — for movie night.

"I don't think you should," Maman said. "It's a very holy day. The Jews don't go out except to walk to synagogue and back."

"You mean I have to be trapped inside, doing nothing? On my birthday?"

Dark circles under Maman's eyes made her look older than her thirty-eight years, more worn out than she normally did. "Daddy won't be back from the Golan for a few days. What if something happens?"

"Nothing will happen," my brother said. "That's the point. It's my birthday, and nothing will happen. It will be another boring day in Israel, far away from my real friends." It was his trump card: *This is boring. Everything is boring. I wish we'd never come here.*

My brother's plan was making me nervous. I wanted to stay with him on his birthday, but I didn't want to get in trouble with our Orthodox neighbours.

Part of me hoped Maman would tell us to work on our correspondence courses. I was doing the grade seven Ontario curriculum, while Etienne was doing grade nine. At the end of each week, we mailed all our work to a teacher in Belleville, who marked it and sent it back by military post.

"*J'sais pas quoi faire.*" Maman rubbed the bone on her wrist joint as if it were a good luck charm. "Your father told me we should all stay inside. Why don't we just eat cake and play Monopoly?"

I would have said yes, but Etienne was adamant. "I want to celebrate with Roberto."

Had Daddy been there, Maman would have won the argument. But it was two against one.

"Go then," she said. "*J'ai pas la force de m'astiner.* But you'll have to walk. No buses running today."

We slipped out the door before she could change her mind. The Herreras lived close to the MAC House. To get there, we'd have to walk through our residential neighbourhood and down the main boulevard, then take a shortcut up a grassy hill with steps cut into the rock. It was only a half-hour walk, but I didn't feel safe doing it alone. The last time we took that route, we found yellow-and-black scorpions, their tails full of poison, sunning themselves on the rocks.

The streets were empty. Maman had been right: no traffic at all. If we'd been older, we might have known better and retreated into the apartment. But we carried on.

Even though it was the end of September, it was a sunny day, hotter than Yellowknife in high summer. We both wore our usual T-shirts and shorts, ankle socks and sneakers. My underarms grew moist as soon as we stepped away from the palm and cypress trees that lined the sidewalk.

It felt strange to be the only ones on the street, as if it were the middle of the night, with everyone else sleeping. When we passed the synagogue, we heard chanting from inside. Curious how it compared to a Catholic church, I looked up at the windows, but they were too high.

"Funny," my brother said. "They're all sitting in there in the dark. You'd think they'd want the lights on."

I shrugged. "Who knows?"

In Yellowknife, there hadn't been a single Jew or Arab that I knew of, not even a Black person. There were Whites, Inuit, Dogrib, and Dene. We had lived in a residential neighbourhood with all the other officers' families. The Native people lived together in a separate community on the outskirts of town, in Rainbow Valley. Most Inuit lived in settlements further north, where they could hunt and fish. Every now and then we would meet one of them at the post office or the general store. We smiled our greetings, but mostly kept to ourselves. In three years, I hadn't made a single First Nations friend. I didn't know any of them by name, because they didn't attend my school or come to Girl Guide meetings.

"Wait up," I called. My brother's legs were longer, his stride quicker. I wasn't sure I could remember the route if I lost sight of him. I was also hoping we could talk as friends. Etienne constantly shut me out, as if he'd drawn a line between us as distinct as the male/female roles in our house. Maman and I took care of the kitchen and the cleaning, while he and Daddy took out the garbage, did any repairs, and looked after the car. We were only two years apart, yet separated by a cavernous rift. We didn't even look related.

From behind, I saw the first rock fly through the air and hit my brother on the shoulder. The second one bounced off his thigh.

"Hey!" he called. "Quit it!"

"It's not me," I shouted, wanting to hide but also wanting to catch up to him.

The pebbles started whizzing now, too many to count. One hit me on the side of the face, near my ear. Etienne had his arms up around his head like the time he'd been attacked by swarming hornets on a camping trip at Great Slave Lake. Angry voices yelled at us from inside the nearest apartment building. We ran down the centre of the street and around the corner, to the main road.

"What was that all about?" Etienne asked. A thin line of blood trickled down from his forehead. It made me think of the strawberry juice that had stained his chin at breakfast.

"I almost lost my glasses." I pulled them off to check that the lenses and frame were intact. "What do you think those people were saying?"

"They sure weren't singing 'Happy Birthday.'" He kept walking. Every now and then he kicked at the edge of the sidewalk. I stared at the spray of dirt on his right sleeve and rubbed the sore spot near my ear.

"Don't tell Maman," he said over his shoulder. "If she finds out, she'll have a fit."

"I won't."

Etienne had more to lose than I did, since he went exploring every day and had made friends with other boys whose fathers were UN peacekeepers. But I was shy and introverted.

Besides roller skating around the perimeter of the apartment building, my only outings were to the market with my mother. "Some holiday," he said, a few minutes later. "Not allowed to go outside or put the lights on, but allowed to throw rocks."

We covered the rest of the distance, about twenty minutes, at a half-walk/half-jog, sticking to the tree-lined main streets and away from the residential areas. I kept my head down, eyes focused on my brother's shoes directly in front of me. I willed my feet to carry me faster, to get me to the Herreras' unscathed. But it was a steady uphill climb, and my lungs felt constricted, letting in only a whistle of air at a time. The quiet was ghostly, like in the Westerns my dad liked to watch: the moment just before the showdown, when the villain walks down the main street, hand on his holster, but all the towns-folk, even the good guy, are hiding, holding their breath.

One street away from the Herreras' house, we came across a bird on the pavement. Its left wing was fanned out at a funny angle, immobile, while the other fluttered frantically. I wanted to move it off the road, to prevent it from getting hit by a car once the traffic started up again.

"No." Etienne was as insistent as he'd been with Maman. "If you touch the bird's feathers, you'll taint it. The flock will reject it."

"They've already abandoned it," I protested. "If we don't help, it's guaranteed to die." But Etienne had walked away. Soon he would be turning the corner.

Once I caught up with him, I looked back. I'd hoped to see the bird lift itself off the street with its one able wing. But it remained pinned in place.

When we got to the Herreras' house, a brick duplex on the corner of a residential street, we leaned in to knock at the same time. The sharpness of the sound made me feel like an intruder.

The front door opened a crack. Then a hand reached through, grabbed my brother's arm, and pulled him inside. I followed. The door closed behind us, and we stood a moment in front of Immaculata, Roberto's eighteen-year-old sister, before anyone spoke. I was wheezing heavily, but my brother, always more athletic than me, breathed normally.

Immaculata was wearing an apron over her pyjamas and had earphones in her ears, attached to a portable cassette player in her apron pocket. She tugged at the earphones and let them fall around her neck. Her eyebrows and eyes went from puzzled to worried and curious before she stepped forward and kissed us hurriedly on both cheeks. Her skin smelled like warm caramel.

"What are you doing here? Are you okay? Is your family okay?" She asked the questions as if anticipating a tragedy. "*Dios mio*, you're panting. Did you run here?" Her Spanish accent made all the words come out in a lilting, melodic way that I found entrancing.

"I came over to see Roberto." Etienne's eyes lingered on Immaculata's face. She was incredibly beautiful, with violet eyes and long dark hair down to her waist.

I started to feel dizzy and nauseous.

"On Yom Kippur?" she asked. "Are you crazy? Everyone is supposed to stay inside and repent for their sins."

"What sins?" My brother grinned.

I leaned against the wall and closed my eyes to let the dizziness pass. In my mind, I saw the wooden confessional booth at the back of St. Pat's in Yellowknife; how we had to wait in line, then kneel in front of the screen and recite our sins to Father Vachon, who listened on the other side. I always practised what to say ahead of time, my heart pulsing, even though I knew he would forgive me no matter what I had done. That was his job. "Three Hail Marys and an Our Father" was his standard response. I wondered what my father, who always went first, might have had to confess. It was a dirty business, all of us sinners standing in line like that, whispering our failings into the saintly priest's ear.

"How will you get home?" Immaculata asked.

Etienne shrugged. "What were you listening to?" He liked rock bands like Kiss and Meatloaf.

"A message from Papa Juan Pablo," she said.

"Your father?" My brother's voice was a bit higher than usual.

"The pope," she said. "A sermon by John Paul II." Her cheeks turned pink. "My fiancé sent it to me."

A gasp of surprise slipped out of me. Engaged! Immaculata was only six years older than me, but a world apart. Marriage was for adults, not kids like us.

"Oh." Etienne leaned against the wall and kept staring.

"The pope visited Buenos Aires," Immaculata said, "for the Feast of the Annunciation. Carlos — my fiancé — went to hear him preach."

This was more religion than we'd ever had in one day. We did weekly Mass, but that was it.

"All French Canadians are Catholic, *si?*" Immaculata asked.

"Yes," I answered. "My father trained to become a missionary priest with the *Oblats de Marie-Immaculée.*" I drew out the syllables to be sure that Immaculata caught the connection to her name. This part of my dad's history wasn't something I'd ever been proud of before. It hadn't seemed important.

"But he was kicked out," Etienne said, "for bad behaviour. He joined the army instead."

I laughed in embarrassment. "Good thing for us, or we would never have been born." It was something I'd thought about many times — how one decision could alter the course of a life.

Roberto came around the corner and grinned when he saw us. "You're just in time to eat." He was sixteen and taller than my brother, and had the same dark-skinned, exotic good looks as Immaculata. He was wearing sport shorts and a soccer shirt with ARGENTINA printed across the front in large gold lettering. I wanted him to kiss us on both cheeks like his sister had done, except that I could smell body odour coming from my damp T-shirt. If he leaned in close enough to me, he would smell it too. But instead of kissing, he punched us both on the arm.

"And after lunch, we'll play Risk," he said.

"I'm going to win," Etienne said. "It's my birthday."

"It's Ronnie Raygun's birthday too," Roberto said. "I heard it on the news last night. He's very popular in Israel."

"So am I." My brother flexed his biceps.

Roberto punched him on the arm again, and my brother stretched out his leg to trip him.

"You'll have to stay with us until sunset." Immaculata stepped away from the wrestling boys. She motioned for me to follow her down the hall toward the kitchen.

"Why sunset?" I asked.

"That's when the Yom Kippur fast ends, and people can move about again."

I wondered how she knew all this. What else didn't I know? If we came home after dark, Maman would be frantic. But there was no way to reach her; the Herreras did not have a telephone. We'd told her where we were going. She could always come and get us with the car. But in the few weeks since our arrival, she'd only taken the car out once. It had stalled several times going up Tiberias's steep streets, and she'd come back saying she'd rather walk — that she'd never be able to drive standard in Israel.

The kitchen was fragrant with the aroma of toasted cheese sandwiches. "We're keeping all the windows shut, with the drapes drawn," Immaculata said. "That way, we can talk and walk around inside the house and no one will know. We've been planning our Christmas trip." She buttered some more bread and put it in the pan to fry.

"Where are you going?" My breathing had returned to normal, but my face was burning. It always turned red after vigorous exercise, and would take a long time to fade.

Immaculata gestured toward the table. It was covered in maps and guidebooks of Israel. "Bethlehem. What better place to celebrate *Navidad?*" Her question sounded like a bar of music. She gathered the papers and books into a pile and placed it in a basket on the floor.

"Mmhmm." I was thirsty and hungry, keen to sink my teeth into a sandwich.

The boys had followed us into the kitchen. "We've been there already," Etienne said, as if he were talking about a new theme park or a restaurant that had just opened. He leaned his arms on the back of one of the chairs.

I could tell what he was thinking: BORING. But he had enough sense not to say it. I'd found the Church of the Nativity gaudy and overwhelming, everything lacquered in gold and heavily ornamented. I'd stood over a small star in the floor, said to mark the place where Jesus had been born, and I felt nothing except hunger.

"We are going there for *Nochebuena* — Christmas Eve," Roberto said.

"On pilgrimage." The glass cross on Immaculata's neck caught the light from the overhead bulb and glittered against her glossy skin.

"*Quin se encuentra aquí?*" a woman's voice called from the hallway. "Who's here?"

Mrs. Herrera came into the kitchen. She was tall like Roberto, and her beautiful face was an older version of Immaculata's. Her hair was pinned up, and she wore a dress with stockings and pumps in spite of the heat. She kissed first my brother then me on both cheeks and took her place at the table. I wanted to ask what a pilgrimage required, but now that my friends' elegant mother was there, I felt shy and didn't want to risk looking even more ignorant.

"*Tiempo para orar,*" she said. "Time to pray."

The Herreras all bowed their heads, but Etienne kept his eyes open and his back straight.

"*Jesús, controla mi vida. Inscribe mi nombre en el libro de la vida, amen.* This is what the Jews hope for today," Mrs. Herrera said. "That their repentance would blot out their sins, and that their names would be written in the Book of Life."

The rest of us digested this piece of information in silence. I wondered if my name was written in the Book of Life. I pictured a feathery pen and a massive, dog-eared book with pages of crinkly onion-skin paper, my name written in calligraphy under my father's, my mother's, and Etienne's.

Mrs. Herrera poured tea for herself, then looked at me. "You walked here? From your apartment in the Orthodox quarter? Dressed like that?"

Though I was relieved that my bare legs were hidden under the table, I wished I could wrap myself in the table-cloth before leaving. Maman insisted that I continue to dress the way I had in Canada. Despite my father's protests, she said the rules of the Jews, made by men to suppress women, didn't apply to us. I hadn't yet heard another foreign woman express a different opinion. How to defend my mother's point of view to Mrs. Herrera?

She turned to my brother. "There is blood on your forehead."

Etienne puffed out his chest and tugged at his shirtsleeve to show the spray of dirt. "We had to run for cover."

"They threw stones at you?" Immaculata asked.

"Yes," he said. "But we dodged them." He flashed her a

smile. Roberto looked my brother up and down the way I might if I envied another girl's clothes and hair. I noticed a medallion attached to a small chain around Roberto's neck that must have been hidden under his soccer shirt earlier. It showed a man in priest's robes with a halo around his head. He was bending over to feed a fox out of his hand.

"I was also hit. In the face," I blurted. Surely our opponents' offences — throwing stones at foreign children walking through their neighbourhood — far outweighed my minor offence of wearing shorts.

Mrs. Herrera bent over her food, her forehead creased in a complex map of intersecting lines. "The Hasidim — the Orthodox community — live devoted lives. In their eyes, you desecrated their most holy day."

Under the table, someone kicked me in the shin. "Agh!" I cried out, but Mrs. Herrera and Immaculata must have thought I was responding to her instruction because neither of them registered surprise. I was sure the kick had been intended for one of the boys, but somehow my leg had gotten in the way.

Mrs. Herrera kept talking. "I admire their piety — their love for God and His laws." She paused and took a sip of her tea. "I would like to put some peroxide on your wounds. Roberto can lend you a clean shirt."

My brother and I concentrated on our sandwiches.

"Mama, they've been to Bethlehem," Immaculata said. She turned to me. "What was it like?" Her thickly lashed eyes searched my face. "The Saviour's birthplace must be wonderful."

I grabbed the glass of water in front of me. I felt intensely thirsty, and emptied the contents of the glass before replying. "The church is huge, but you practically have to crawl to get through the door."

"The Door of Humility," Mrs. Herrera said. As much as I'd craved her attention and concern only a few minutes earlier, now that she was listening intently, I wanted to slip under the table. My palms were sweating. It was hot and stuffy in the house with all the windows shut, the curtains drawn, and five of us in the smallish room. I chewed the bread as long as I could and swallowed slowly, then poured myself another glass of water.

"It's fancy inside." I hoped that was what they wanted to hear. It was nothing like the hay-filled stable described in the Bible story.

"Did you walk from Jerusalem?" Immaculata asked.

I remembered the sweltering heat of the city. How I'd gotten heat stroke and had to be brought back to the hotel. How dizzy and disoriented I'd felt. "No," I said. "We drove."

"It's only ten kilometres from the Old City," Immaculata said. "They say you can do it in two hours at a brisk pace, but we plan to take our time. There could be up to one hundred thousand pilgrims."

I wondered if Roberto was as keen on religion as his sister and mother, but his face was blank. Etienne was studying what was left of his sandwich as if it were the most interesting thing he'd ever seen. I knew what he'd say as soon as we were alone: "These people are crazy." But I wasn't sure I'd agree. Other than my grandmother and Father Vachon, I'd never met anyone with such a devoted Catholic faith. There was something deeply comforting and attractive about it. I wanted to believe that God was watching over me.

"It's a UNESCO World Heritage site," Mrs. Herrera added. "Possibly the oldest church in the world."

I picked up the crumbs on my plate one at a time with moistened fingers.

After lunch, Roberto brought out his handmade Risk game. It had caricatures of all the United Nations kids in the spaces representing their various countries. Each face was drawn in blue ink. The countries were labelled in large block letters, next to their respective flags. My caricature featured my long braids, glasses, shaggy bangs, and large teeth. Hardly flattering, but not bad for a freestyle drawing with a ballpoint pen. If it had been drawn a year earlier, my teeth would have been crooked, leaning awkwardly against one another like slats of a broken fence.

Next to my brother, I looked homely and plain. In his caricature, he was flexing his huge biceps. On his T-shirt were the words Mr. Universe. He had a small head compared to his inflated chest, but wore a wide grin. A maple leaf was tattooed on his forearm. Roberto was drawn as a soccer star, a ball under his arm and another under his foot, while Immaculata smiled angelically, her eyes half the size of her face.

We played all afternoon. I was the first to get eliminated, at the beginning of the second hour when I gambled my men and armies for a piece of land in central Europe. Immaculata was more conservative, but we were no match for the boys, who had played this game nearly every day since Roberto and Johan had designed their hand-drawn copy. From time to time, Roberto pulled back the blind on the window and peered out. The street was deserted. I thought of Maman alone at the apartment. How quiet it would be there.

The sun began to set after seven-thirty. From close by, a horn sounded.

"That's the *shofar*. The fast is finished. You can go home now." Immaculata got up to stretch. She was still in her pyjamas.

"Anyway, I've just about conquered the world." Etienne shook the dice and threw them onto the table. A scowling Roberto lined up his tiny plastic artillery across the continent of South America.

"But it will be dark," I said, suddenly afraid, not just of walking home, but also of facing my mother.

As if she'd read my thoughts, Immaculata responded, "We'll ask Mama to drive you. We'll come with you."

She disappeared down the hallway, calling her mother's name, and reemerged a few minutes later in form-fitting jeans and a purple T-shirt the same shade as her eyes. My brother stared at her, the game momentarily forgotten as she brushed her long hair with smooth, even strokes.

Mrs. Herrera opened the front door and a rush of cool evening air filled the room. People had begun to mill about on the sidewalk. Blinds were lifted, lamps lit. The curfew was over. I hoped Maman would have our apartment windows open. Mrs. Herrera swept her eyes over my face. "Your wound is not so angry and red. It should heal quickly."

But her face betrayed worry in a distinct line across her forehead.

The boys, still talking about my brother's victory at Risk, climbed into the back seat of the car. Roberto and I sat hip to hip, my knee pressed into his thigh, my arm brushing his soccer shirt. I looked out the window, wondering if he could smell my hair and my perspiration, and what it would be like to hold his hand.

"I will wait here until you are safely inside," Mrs. Herrera said when we arrived at our apartment building. A number of people had gathered in the street. Black-clad men stood together on one side, women in head scarves on the other, while small children milled about between the two groups. Everyone ignored us. If they'd seen us walking earlier that morning, breaking their rules, they didn't let on. They were intent on their celebration. The girls my age were in two lines, facing each other, playing a game with a ball. They grew quiet as Etienne and I entered the walkway. Etienne sauntered through ahead of me, head held high as if daring everyone to look at him. He even said hi to the girls on either end, who blushed and giggled before turning their faces away.

Then it was my turn. There was no other entrance, and the girls weren't moving. To get to the safety of home, I had to run this gauntlet, down the gangplank of black-eyed, stony-faced girls in their full skirts and long-sleeved shirts. I could smell their candy breath as I passed. My bare legs and arms burned with shame, as if I were parading naked. I blinked back the tears, fixing my eyes on the stairwell leading down to our apartment. Mrs. Nouger, my grade six teacher in Yellowknife, would have been furious if something like this had ever happened in the school playground at Mildred Hall, where she insisted that no one be left out of our games. But there was nothing to do but keep walking, then take the stairs two at a time.

Maman was waiting for us at the door. She wasn't wearing the pyjamas and housecoat she would usually slip into after supper, but was fully dressed. She even had her shoes on. "You're home you're home you're home!" She hugged me so tightly I thought the buttons on the front of her dress might leave an imprint on my skin. "I should never have let you go. I almost went driving around to find you, but I was too scared to go out alone."

After she stopped hugging me, she kept her face close to mine. I realized I was now taller than her. It must have happened in the last few weeks, since we'd left Canada. Her shoulders were narrower than mine. I probably weighed more too.

"Mrs. Herrera drove us home as soon as the sun went down. We weren't sure what else to do." I wanted to tell her about the girls upstairs, but she already looked so small and helpless.

"We were stoned," Etienne blurted. "Near the synagogue."

"*Lapidé! Mon Dieu!*" Her hands fluttered to her hair, her face, the front of her dress. She reminded me of the panicky injured bird we had seen earlier that day. Had it died on the road? I wished I had ignored my brother and scooped it up.

Maman took in every part of me, as if I were a message on a roadside billboard. Then she pulled a matchbook out of her dress pocket and moved to the table, where she'd placed a double-layer chocolate cake. Her fingers trembled as she lit the match. Its small light wobbled over the fourteen candles. "Make a wish."

My stomach felt sour, but Etienne bent over his cake. The light of the candles danced on his face, illuminating pimples, dirt, and sweat.

"But we haven't sung to him," I protested.

"I don't have the energy to sing," Maman said.

Etienne blew out the candles, and my mother served the cake. I looked around the kitchen for evidence of a meal, but the counters were clean. If Maman had eaten, she'd already put everything away.

"I'm still learning to negotiate the oven," she said, as we lifted our forks to our mouths. "Kind of like the Peugeot's stick shift on the Tiberias hills." She looked worried as she watched us chew.

The cake was hard and dry, but the icing was good. I forced myself to eat the whole piece. It gave me time to prepare what I wanted to say next. "It was a bad idea to let us go. A mistake."

"I only did it because it was Etienne's birthday." My mother sounded defeated. "I couldn't force him to stay in and do nothing all day."

"You shouldn't have let me go out in shorts." I looked down at the curve of my thigh. "I wish I'd known."

"We're Canadians. Not Israelis," Maman said. "You're just a twelve-year-old girl. You wear what you want."

Music wafted in through the open window, followed by loud clapping and whistling. The dancing had started up again.

"Next time I go out, I'm wearing a skirt."

"Their rules don't apply to us," Maman said. "We're different."

"I don't want to be different," I answered. "I want to fit in."

"Good luck with that," Etienne said, his mouth full of his second piece of cake. "It'll never happen."

I wanted to shake off his words, wipe them away like crumbs.

"I know who's to blame for the shelled peanuts on the sofa," Maman said.

"I told you it wasn't me," I said, happy to have the accusation lifted.

But my mother was pointing a broom at the stove. "There's a huge rat hiding behind there. And it's got a nest full of babies in the storage closet." She handed the broom to my brother. "You've got to kill the mother and the babies, or we'll be infested."

Vomit rose up the back of my throat.

"I've been listening to it rattle around in the kitchen all day," Maman said. "The building was so quiet I could hear every move it made."

"Some birthday." Etienne still hadn't budged. "What if I corner it and it bites me?"

"We have no choice," my mother answered. "There's no other way." She tried to hand me the dustpan, but I backed out of the kitchen and ran for refuge in my room.

I wanted Etienne to kill the rats, but I didn't have the stomach to be his accomplice. I put my pillow over my head to drown out the dying animal's desperate shrieks.

My father at his observation post overlooking No Man's Land on the Golan Heights, October 1982.

~

SURPRISE

~

*For all living things in nature must unfold in
their particular way and become themselves at
any cost and despite all opposition.*

RAINER MARIA RILKE
LETTERS TO A YOUNG POET

"I brought something home for you from the Golan," Daddy
said.

"Israeli chocolate?" It was my favourite food.

"Fresh figs," Maman guessed.

"A goatskin tent like the Bedouin live in!" Etienne said. "Or
one of the knives they use for skinning."

Daddy shook his head no after each guess.

"A day pass to the spa at the Tiberias Hotel?" Maman's
face lit up with hope. She'd spent the last few days washing
sheets, scouring the apartment, and cooking a meal of roasted
chicken and Israeli couscous in preparation for Daddy's

homecoming. That morning she'd woken up early to curl her hair. She'd knocked on my bedroom door to ask if the cream she'd put under her eyes covered the dark circles from reading late each night. She was used to Daddy's frequent absences, but I could tell that these prolonged peacekeeping missions were hard for her.

Daddy reached into his large wicker picnic basket and pulled out a pickle jar filled with grass and leaves. He held it up so we could see. Etienne and I inched closer, while Maman recoiled and sank back into the couch, as if afraid that my father might drop this treasure into her lap. A large black insect slithered into view.

"It's a rare find," Daddy said, "a Middle Eastern millipede." He set the jar down in the centre of the coffee table. We watched the creature ooze black slime on the leaves and grasses.

"Let's take it out." Etienne reached for the lid, but my father pushed the jar out of his reach.

"It could spray a chemical into your eyes, or spread poison on your skin. We have no idea."

"I want to show this to Roberto and Johan!" Etienne said.

"This is disgusting and dangerous," Maman said. "It has no place in our home." Before Etienne or Daddy could stop her, she grabbed the jar and walked onto the porch.

"Hey!" Daddy called. "What are you doing?"

She unscrewed the lid and threw the many-legged monster into the grassy Galilean valley.

"No one will believe me now," Etienne said, heading for his room. The bed squeaked as he flopped his weight onto it.

"What other surprises did you bring back from the Golan?" Maman asked. "Besides dirty laundry and dishes?"

"I'll tell you at supper." Daddy carried his wicker basket, the size of a large camping cooler, into the kitchen, then headed for the bathroom. "I haven't had a bath in ten days. Being the woman on the observation post wiped me out."

It was hard to imagine Daddy as a housekeeper, but on one of his twice-monthly stints on the Golan with another United Nations officer, he did the female chores and his partner the male. Then the next time, they switched. When it was my father's turn to be the "woman," as they called it, he had to provide the meals for the week while his partner observed the no man's land that divided Syria and Israel.

I leaned against the wall in the hallway and watched my father arrange the contents of his shaving kit on the small counter next to the sink.

"We ate like kings though," he said.

"Thanks to me," my mother called from the kitchen. The men were competitive about who provided the best meals. Preparation for my father's biweekly trips involved advance baking and shopping, as well as extensive coaching from Maman, since she did all the cooking in our family.

"Did you see anything?" Etienne looked up from his magazine.

"Nothing much," Daddy said. "A few Druze. A bunch of Bedouin shepherds."

"So you watched the Bedouin while they watched their sheep?"

"More or less. It was pretty quiet out there." My father ran the water into the tub and shut the bathroom door. Etienne slipped outside, probably in search of the critter. I wandered into the kitchen to see what Maman was doing.

She squirted dish soap into the sink and rolled up her sleeves. "Help me empty this." She pointed at the hamper. I pulled out half a dozen empty bottles of wine and threw them into the trash, then reached for a dish towel and positioned myself next to my mother at the kitchen sink. She reached up to tuck a loose strand behind her ear. The steam from the sink was making her hair limp and straight, without a trace of the morning's bouncy curls.

Later that afternoon, I was playing my recorder in my room when Maman suggested that Etienne and I walk up to the Herreras' house to see if they were home.

"I want to, but ..." My fingernail picked at the small scab on my face, near my ear. The skin was healing, but the memory was fresh.

"That won't happen again," Maman said. "It will be good for you to get out." I wondered if she might be trying to get rid of us.

I changed out of my shorts into jeans and stuffed my recorder into my backpack along with my journal and my Judy Blume novel. I was trying to write down the details of our daily lives, the way a real writer would. As for the recorder, I wanted to showcase my skills with Immaculata, who played classical piano for her mother every afternoon at teatime. Last visit, we'd made a deal: I would teach her some basic recorder, and she would show me how to play something on the piano. "Stick together," Maman said. She gave us each a few shekels.

We used the money to ride the crowded bus as far as it could take us, then walked up a flight of steps that gave us a view of the lake and town tucked into the hill below. I lifted my face to the breeze and raised my arms to let the wind go through my clothes and cool me off. "Watch for scorpions," Etienne said. "They're all over the place." I looked down at my sandalled feet, ready to bolt, but Etienne was peering intently into the tall grass, parting tufts as if hoping to tease them out.

"Let's get going."

"No." Etienne squatted on the step, his eyes fixed on the grass. He pulled a piece of honey candy out of his pocket, unwrapped it, and laid it on the cement. "You want to see something cool?"

Daddy had warned us about scorpions, how the poison in their stingers could kill a child. "It goes directly into your blood stream, like snake venom, and kills you within an hour," he'd said. Since then, we always shook out our shoes in the morning before putting them on.

Etienne pulled out his red Swiss army pocketknife. "They're attracted to sugar. But Daddy told me what to do when I find one." My chest tightened with the familiar jealousy, like a coiled snake inside me. For the thousandth time, I wished I'd been born a boy. I wondered what else Daddy had told my brother, and why he hadn't bothered to tell me. All those father-son fishing trips in Yellowknife still rankled.

I wanted to be my father's chosen companion, and the keeper of his secrets.

"Here it comes." Etienne parted the grass at the edge of the step, and a yellow scorpion skittered out. I ran up a couple of steps to watch from a safe distance. Etienne waited for the deadly arachnid to make its way to the candy, then pulled the tiny scissors out of his knife set. With a steady hand, he clipped the end of the insect's tail. The ball of venom fell off and rolled into the grass. "Without his pistol he's just a plaything." Etienne grinned at me, then stuck out his finger and let the scorpion climb onto his arm.

"I want to go," I said. I'd forgotten to wear a hat, and the sun was making me dizzy. "You're grossing me out."

"But it's so cute! Maybe I'll keep it as a pet." Now the scorpion was climbing up his shoulder. Soon it would be in his hair.

Etienne stood, shook the scorpion free, and watched it land on its back on the cement step. Just as it was righting itself, he lifted his foot and crushed it.

I told myself it was just a big spider. But a weight settled on my chest just the same.

"Now I'm ready," Etienne said, and ran up the steps two at a time. One of his legs was shorter than the other, and he was supposed to wear a shoe with a raised heel. He hated it. He said it make him look like he was handicapped. "Just be glad you have two legs," my mother told him. At fifteen, she'd been diagnosed with polio and was told she would use a wheelchair for the rest of her life. I'd often wondered what would have happened if she hadn't stubbornly insisted on training her legs to walk again during the six months she'd been hospitalized. Would she have married my father? Would Etienne and I have been born? Maybe my brother had outgrown his special shoe, or it hadn't made it into our luggage, but I realized that I hadn't seen him wear it even once since we'd arrived in Israel. I wanted to race after him and pass him on the stairs, to gain the upper hand somehow, even though I needed him to show me the way to the Herreras'. I hated having to walk behind, to be younger and less competent. I hated the way the blood rushed to my face whenever I did physical activity. It took a long time for my colour to return to normal, beginning with a circle of white around my mouth. It was hideous.

When we got to the Herreras' house, Roberto was waiting for us outside, a skateboard tucked under each arm. "Let's go up to the big parking lot," he said to Etienne. "My sister is in the house," he called to me over his shoulder.

Three hours later, Etienne and I headed back down toward the Orthodox quarter. I played the first four bars of "Für Elise" on an invisible keyboard while I hummed the notes. "I wonder what Daddy's second surprise is going to be," I said as we neared our apartment. "Maybe we're going on a trip to Damascus or back to Jerusalem."

"Maybe we're going home."

"I doubt it." We'd only been here a bit more than a month.

The announcement came while we were eating our dessert. "I've hired a music tutor." My father cleaned the ice cream off his moustache with the edge of his napkin. "A Belgian captain I met on the Golan. He'll be here in a few minutes."

"Music is part of a comprehensive education," Maman said. "It will add to your homeschooling." She looked at my father as if he were a magician with a sleeve full of tricks.

Etienne groaned, but I was delighted. In Yellowknife, my brother had played the trumpet in the junior high band. I learned the recorder at school. In grade six, I was the only alto player in the recorder ensemble. My teacher praised my musical ability and taught me the alternate fingering and scales.

"The trumpet is a fine military instrument," my father declared in response to Etienne's displeasure. "We use it as a call to arms, to sound the alarm, or to mourn the dead in battle. I've asked Capitaine Latulipe to teach you to play 'Taps.'"

"*Day is done, gone the sun,*" I sang. "*From the lakes, from the hills, from the sky. All is well, safely rest, God is nigh.* We used to sing it at the end of the day at Girl Guide camp."

"Yeah," Etienne said, "and at Scout meetings." He looked at the door as if considering his options.

A few minutes later, there was a sharp knock, and my father rose to answer. The tutor, a thin man with pouched eyes who spoke feathery European French, worked with my brother first. He entered Etienne's room and shut the door behind him. I wanted to listen in; I'd hoped we'd be taught together, so that I might learn the trumpet too, and perhaps even play a rousing military march to please my father.

After half an hour, it was my turn. I laid my newly

polished instrument out on my bed, alongside the creased paper that showed the alto fingering. The tutor sat down beside me and waved an impatient hand. *"Joue moi la gamme de do."* He closed his eyes.

It took me a minute to understand. *Play me the scale of Doe.* "Doe?" I asked. I glanced over at the fingering chart. It had fluttered to the floor when he'd sat down on my bed. I searched for Doe, but saw only letters: C, F, B-flat, D.

"How many sharps or flats?" I asked in English, since I didn't know the musical terms in French.

"Quoi? Do. Joue Do." He pulled a metronome out of his shirt pocket and clapped to the beat. *"Un deux trois quatre.* Keep this speed," he said in faltering English.

My stomach did its familiar nervous squeeze. I felt my face go red and hot. The tutor stood up from my bed, brushed his pants as if to rid himself of any invisible pests that might have landed on him, and walked out the door.

"I cannot work with her," he said to my mother. I could hear them talking in the hallway. I was too disappointed and embarrassed to leave my room.

"I don't understand," my mother said in French. "She loves her instrument so much."

"She lacks even the most rudimentary skills. And her instrument is not orchestral, but folklorish."

There was a pause, and then my father's voice. "Would you like a glass of wine? *Un digestif?"*

"Non, merci," the tutor said.

I wanted to put my bedspread over my head and cry. But instead, I picked up my instrument and played the Irish ballad my grade six class had performed for the graduation ceremonies. My fingers were shaky, and the high C wobbled a bit, but the familiar melody helped to release the knot in my gut. I closed my eyes and played it again, this time from memory. I pictured Catherine beside me and Mrs. Avery at the front, with her impossibly high heels and her conductor's baton, which she would forget to wave halfway through the song, explaining to us later that it was because the music had overwhelmed her with the strength of its beauty. "It's why we play," she liked to say. "Music is transformative."

"My son is not so keen on lessons," Maman said to Capitaine Latulipe. "He's the athlete in the family. Our daughter is the ..."

"I will do as the major requested," came the answer. "I will teach the boy."

I waited for Maman to ask him to give me another chance, or at least to comment on the beauty of the melody I'd played. But there was only the sound of a man's footsteps on the tiled floor, the door opening and closing, and wine being poured into a glass.

~

FRIENDS
AND ENEMIES

~

Monday morning found Tom Sawyer miserable.

MARK TWAIN
THE ADVENTURES OF TOM SAWYER

Overlooking the shores of the Sea of Galilee, in the heart
of the tourist district, the Tiberias Hotel towered over the
other hotels on Gdud Barak Road. Its large outdoor pool,
surrounded by lush banana and coconut trees, was reserved
exclusively for hotel guests and United Nations personnel
and their families.

"I could almost make myself believe I'm a tourist," Maman
said, accepting a pile of plush beach towels from the attendant
while Daddy paid the fee at the front desk.

We claimed lounge chairs next to the O'Shaughnessys, an
Irish family whose father worked for the UN.

"I feel rich," Etienne said.

Maman adjusted her wide-brimmed sun hat and started chatting with pretty Molly O'Shaughnessy, whose pink lipstick matched her bikini. With her hair pulled back into a ponytail, she looked much younger than Maman. She kept an eye on her husband and children while she spoke.

Patrick O'Shaughnessy was a hunk: he had a slim, athletic body, with muscular arms and chest. His dark wavy hair was the same colour as his wife's, making the two appear a natural pair. He scooped up one of their two-year-old twins and stuffed him under his arm, then chased the other curly-headed toddler around the side of the pool. "Two twenty-pound sacks of taters!" he said when he'd caught them both.

I remembered my father with a bushy beard, coming back to Canada after one of his long absences in Egypt, lifting me high in his arms. I must have been a very small child, he seemed so tall and large to me. He said my name and held me against his chest for a long time.

Daddy removed his shirt and unfolded his newspaper. I stretched out on a chair next to him and bent one knee to make my legs look more shapely, according to the poolside advice I'd read about in a teen magazine.

Lara O'Shaughnessy, the twins' older sister, was a few chairs down, deep into a book. She was two years younger than me, and even shyer. I couldn't tell if she was ignoring me because of shyness or if she was so engrossed in her book that she hadn't noticed my arrival. I decided to put off saying hello until later.

"This is the life," Maman said.

"Aye. But Patrick leaves for Beirut tonight." Molly O'Shaughnessy fiddled with the parasol behind her chair. "Part of being a military wife, right?"

Maman glanced over at Daddy. "It's never easy to see our men go. When will he be back?"

"In three weeks — on the twenty-fourth."

Patrick O'Shaughnessy jumped into the shallow end, still holding a squealing twin under each arm.

I thought of the way Maman circled dates on the kitchen calendar and drew hearts and smiley faces around the words "*Retour de Donald*." Daddy's return was always a cause for celebration.

I felt sweaty and hot, but instead of swimming, I hid behind my puzzle book. Sitting on the edge of the pool with their feet in the water were three tanned and gorgeous teenage girls. Their bathing suits were daringly cut: high on the thigh and low on the chest, coming down between their breasts almost to their navels.

My brother had noticed them too. The moment we arrived he had hopped into the pool and swum over to chat with them. We'd only just gotten here and he'd already made friends.

I wished I could be winsome, like him, and know just what to say and how to act. I knew more Hebrew than he did, but attempting to start a conversation with a stranger my age seemed like an insurmountable obstacle.

Etienne and the girls started a game of water basketball.

Maman handed me a bag of salted pretzels. "Those girls don't look anything like the Israeli girls in our building, do they?" she whispered. Since we'd arrived in Tiberias, she'd been remarking on the differences between religious and secular Israelis.

Feeling acutely self-conscious, I went in search of the hotel bathroom. I couldn't help but compare my body, in its modest swimsuit, to the shape of my brother's new friends. I tugged at the edges of my yellow one-piece so that it rose up higher over my thighs and appraised myself in the full-length mirror. In our neighbourhood, I was always the one showing the most skin, while all the other girls my age were covered head to toe in spite of the punishing heat. But today, more than my outfit was wrong. My skin was white, not tanned. With my glasses, braids, and the suit I had used for swimming lessons at the Yellowknife public pool, I didn't look anything like the models in *Seventeen* or the Israeli girls around the pool.

When I got back, there was a girl sitting on my chair, giggling with Etienne. She didn't get up, even when I stood next to her.

"This is Or," Etienne said. "Her name means 'gold.'"

"I know," I said. "It's French."

"*Mon père travaille à l'ambassade française,*" she said in an elegant accent. She uncurled her perfect body, grabbed my brother's hand, and led him off to the poolside restaurant, leaving a wet spot where she'd sat on my towel.

I slipped into the pool, ducked my head underwater to cool off, and imagined holding hands with Johan, my brother's Swedish friend, sipping a milkshake through two straws, our bent foreheads almost touching. I pictured him sketching me while I posed in the sunlight, then reaching over to cradle my face in his hands for my first kiss.

I did the backstroke over to the shallow end. When I turned around, Lara was sitting on the steps.

"It's nice in here," I said. If she didn't answer, I could pretend that my words had been meant for my parents, and gesture to them to come in.

"You're a good swimmer," she said, sniffling. She had a small, round nose that scrunched up like a rabbit's when she sniffed.

"I used to take lessons, back in Canada."

"In Ireland, it's too cold to swim in the sea." She pushed off the bottom step with her feet and dog-paddled over to me, still sniffling. Either she had a bad cold or it was a nervous tic.

"I can teach you some strokes." I liked the feeling of having something to teach. Since we'd arrived in Israel, there had been so much to learn. "Do you know how to do the dead man's float?" I flipped over onto my belly and stretched out my arms and legs in a star. I held my breath underwater until I sensed Lara's body floating next to mine.

"*Ça valait la peine*," my father said, once home from the hotel. My mother beamed.

I thought it was a funny expression to choose: it was worth the trouble. Considering the other trouble in our lives, this was easy street. The next day was a case in point: Monday. School. I would have gladly spent Monday morning closeted in my room with my journal and my books, but my parents insisted that Etienne and I ride the crowded van to the make-shift school where all the UN kids did their correspondence courses side by side.

"Maman, I don't like it," I said while she braided my hair. "I don't want to go. The building looks like it was bombed. It's completely run down and abandoned, except for our classroom."

Etienne scowled at me from the sofa. "You're such a baby."

"You need to see other children." Maman wound an elastic around the end of the braid. "You and Lara O'Shaughnessy looked like you were hitting it off yesterday."

"Yes, but I hate that stuffy minivan," I argued, though she had inadvertently reminded me that one of the only good things about going to school was getting to see Johan. "Did you know we have to sit on each other's laps?"

"You're going." Maman set the brush aside and handed me a water bottle. "Get your book bag."

Our blue-bereted driver, Captain Giggs, slowed the van to a crawl as we entered the empty lot in front of the school, a one-storey, flat-roofed building that looked like an abandoned strip mall. Mrs. Lewis, the Irish officer's wife who was our volunteer teacher, stood by the door as she did each morning. From a distance, her petite frame made her look like a child. She wore her usual plain shoes, knee-length navy skirt, and white blouse, the uniform she'd created for herself. But that morning she stood under a shattered window, surrounded by broken glass.

My pulse beat double time. More trouble.

"Stay in the van," Captain Giggs commanded as he left to check out the situation.

But twenty-five of us were crammed into a twelve-passenger van. The air inside was stale and humid, and my hip ached from being pressed up against the armrest. As soon as the driver left, Johan slid the back door open, complaining, "We need to breathe!" Everyone on the left side tumbled out.

"North against South," Etienne said. The boys began splitting into two basketball teams: the Argentinians, Chileans, and Australians in one group, the Europeans and Canadians in another.

"Don't you want to find out what happened?" Roberto asked.

But Etienne just shrugged. "We'll know soon enough."

Anxious about disobeying the driver's instructions, I stayed close to the van. I glanced over at Lara O'Shaughnessy, still sitting inside with a handful of younger girls, but she didn't look up from her Famous Five mystery. I hated her for ignoring me. She hadn't even said hi when she climbed into the van that morning. But a few minutes later, when the other girls came to stand beside me, she followed. Together, we walked toward our teacher. It wasn't long before the basketball sounds stopped and the boys joined us.

Mrs. Lewis removed the padlock and swung the door open. The classroom had been ransacked, chairs and tables overthrown. There was a pile of foul-smelling dog excrement in the middle of the concrete floor.

"Gross!" Etienne said from the centre of a pack of boys. He made a fist and punched it into his hand. Some of the others did the same.

"Shit!" Johan said. I waited for the teacher to reprimand him, but she didn't.

Lisette, the eleven-year-old from St. Malo, France, held her cloth knapsack in front of her like a shield. Her lower lip trembled. Lara O'Shaughnessy looked down at her feet.

"I'll bring the kids home," Captain Giggs said in his musical New Zealand accent. The tips of his large ears were pink.

"No. We'll start with recess this morning." Mrs. Lewis locked eyes with Captain Giggs, who was twice her size. She then fixed the class with her no-nonsense look. "Roberto, Johan, and Etienne, help me put the desks and chairs back. The rest of you get some fresh air."

None of us moved. I looked back and forth from Mrs. Lewis to Captain Giggs to see who would make the final decision. The uniformed man jingled the coins in his pocket.

Lisette pinched her nose. "What good is a padlocked door if they break the windows?" Her voice came out like a wheeze.

Mrs. Lewis pretended not to hear. She picked up a chair and placed it at the spot where she liked to sit. "We'll have this room back to normal in no time."

"Bring us some cleaning supplies," she told Captain Giggs. "And a large cardboard box and some duct tape." He shrugged and shook his head, but turned to walk toward the van.

"Out you go," she said to the class. "Watch for broken glass. Do not venture into the rooms on the other side of the classroom." She gave us the same instructions each Monday morning, as if the weekend had made us forget. Since we'd started gathering here in late September, the "school grounds" had always been a mess. But never this bad.

"Stay in the car park," she added in her thick Irish brogue.

The boy with the basketball started dribbling it. Most of the kids followed him out the door. Lara blew her nose loudly. I watched the white UN van drive away. All I wanted was to be back on it, driving through Tiberias to the safety of our apartment building on the hill overlooking the lake, where I could do my grade seven curriculum in peace. I could sit at the desk in my small room and lose myself in *The Adventures of Tom Sawyer*, where the greatest danger Tom faced was being caught by his Aunt Polly and getting a licking.

Columns of French verbs and tidy mathematical equations with only one right answer were deeply satisfying. I didn't need anyone to help me solve them. I loved writing out my answers on graph paper, folding them up, and sliding them into the envelopes that would carry them from Israel all the way to Belleville, Ontario, by military mail — a special arrangement for all Canadian military kids living abroad. Mrs. Blackwood, the grade seven teacher, wrote encouraging words at the bottom of each page and sent my work back to me, adorned with stickers and check marks. Her praise made me feel smart and accomplished. I kept the returned envelopes in a box underneath my bed, like a soldier's treasured correspondence with his loved one.

The classroom, with its cement floor and walls, was cool inside. But outside, the Israeli sun pressed down on my head. There was no shade in the parking lot that served as our playground — not a single tree. My stomach clenched. I looked around for Lara and found her deep into a book next to the classroom door, her back pressed against the brick wall. "Can I sit with you?"

"Sure." When she looked up from her book, I could tell she'd been crying. She quickly looked back down again. Her nose did that sniffling, rabbit thing she'd done at the pool.

"Are you scared?" I asked.

Lara nodded.

"Me too," I said. Comforting Lara took a bit of my fear away.

"You picked a good place to read," I said, even though it wasn't comfortable or shady. It was the nicest thing I could think to say. I slid my back down the wall and settled in beside her. We both seemed content not to talk but just to be side by side. The other good thing about my vantage point was that I had a clear view of Johan on the basketball court.

At the top of a clean page in my notebook, I wrote *The Adventures of Tom Sawyer*, by Mark Twain: Book Report in capital letters. Underneath, I wrote Theme: Friendly Warfare, and underlined each word. In my best handwriting, I copied out:

"Tom's army won a great victory, after a long and hard-fought battle. Then the dead were counted, prisoners exchanged, the terms of the next disagreement agreed upon and the day for the necessary battle appointed; after which the armies fell into line and marched away, and Tom turned homeward alone."

— Mark Twain, *The Adventures of Tom Sawyer*

Under the caption "Extended Metaphor," I wrote:

Though the author uses the language of war, with words such as victory, battle, dead, prisoners, and armies, the reader is meant to understand that this is part of Tom's elaborate make-believe world of play.

Then, under "Reader Response," I wrote:

Dear Mrs. Blackwood,
I hate being someone's enemy when I don't even know what I've done wrong. Have you ever been part of a war? I'm stuck in the middle of one, even though my dad came here to keep the peace.

Mrs. Lewis peered over my shoulder. "Mrs. Blackwood is lucky to have you as a student," she said. "She must look forward to reading your work."

Surprised and pleased but too shy to look up, I kept writing.

"One day, I'll see your name in print," Mrs. Lewis continued. "I'll come across your books in a Dublin bookseller's."

I pulled my knees up to my chest and wrapped my arms around them so that my notebook pressed against my heart. Mrs. Lewis's words were the kindest thing anyone had ever said to me.

"You're a writer?" There was a note of respect and awe in Lara's voice.

"It's my dream." I focused on the small buckle on our teacher's black shoes.

"Aye," Mrs. Lewis said softly. "Ye have the gift." She made it sound like I was the keeper of a magic egg or a golden secret.

When she rang her bell to call us back from recess, I moved my book bag and supplies to the desk next to Lara's. I placed my notebook in the top right-hand corner, with the pen balanced in the middle, and Lara did the same.

Mrs. Lewis announced that we would set aside our individual studies for the morning in favour of a group geography lesson. "This will benefit us all," she said. Etienne rolled his eyes at Johan. He hated school, but not for the same reasons I did. He resented having to sit and listen when he could be outside shooting baskets or combing the Israeli countryside for scorpions and scarab beetles.

"You must all be wondering why our schoolroom has been subject to this act of vandalism," Mrs. Lewis continued.

The chemical cleaning products were making my eyes water and my nose itch. I searched in my bag for a tissue. I didn't want anyone to think I was crying.

"This property is situated in a community of African Jewish immigrants, mostly Ethiopians." Mrs. Lewis paused to consider her next words. "These families came to Israel to escape from religious persecution, famine, and civil war in their country. It was difficult for them to get here. Unfortunately, they have not been well received by Israelis. That's why they're forced to live in this kind of ghetto."

"Racism," Roberto said. He had the darkest skin of all of us, including his sister.

"But why do they hate us so much?" Johan's question was exactly what I wanted to know. "We haven't done anything to them."

"Sometimes, when people are persecuted by others, they adopt a defensive attitude to everyone else," Mrs. Lewis answered. "Bullying can become a means of survival. Even for children. Their violence is a result of accumulated frustration."

The room was silent while we took in the new information.

"Who knows what obstacles these people are up against?" Mrs. Lewis held her thermos cup to her face, making her glasses fog. She set it down, then reached for a large map of the world that she taped to the blackboard. "Now who can locate Ethiopia?"

After we'd placed a coloured pin on the map to indicate where the immigrants had come from, we took turns pointing out our country of origin, along with its capital city and major waterways. When it was Johan's turn, he made us practise how to pronounce Sweden in his language. "*Sver-ye*" we repeated.

"How do you spell it?" Johan asked, in a perfect imitation of Mrs. Lewis. The class roared.

My hand shot up. I had several Swedish stamps that Johan's mother had given me for my collection. Under the picture of the queen was the word *Sverige*.

"Miss Canada will come up to the chalkboard and spell it for us," Johan continued in his goofy mock-Irish voice. His blond hair, parted on the side by a cowlick, made him look like a taller, older version of carefree Tom Sawyer.

"We will make you an honorary Swede," Johan said when he saw that I had spelled it correctly. I felt the blood rush to my face. I couldn't get back to my seat fast enough.

Johan was leading the class in a rendition of ABBA's "Super Trooper" when the first pings sounded on the corrugated iron roof. Our voices died down as the noise above us increased. "The drummer is off beat," Johan said. But this time, only a few boys laughed.

The map, grown heavy from all the pins, fluttered to the floor.

Everyone began talking at once. Lara packed up her stuff. Lizette started crying again, louder this time. The pinging on the roof intensified.

"Let's practise our aim," Etienne said. He and Roberto shot their erasers at the blackboard. One of them hit Johan on the shoulder. On his way back to his desk, Johan whipped a piece of chalk at Etienne, then gathered up his books.

Mrs. Lewis picked up the fallen map. "If they wish to discourage or frighten us, we will not give them the satisfaction."

I felt a sudden need to use the bathroom. But to gain access to our small "water closet," as our teacher called it, we had to go outside.

The boy two chairs down bit into an apple. I wished I'd brought more food. Who knew how long we'd be trapped?

A few more pings sounded on the roof, then all was quiet. Mrs. Lewis walked toward the door and put her hand on the knob, turning slowly. She stood in the doorway, framed by the light. "We are here in the name of peace." I wasn't sure if she was addressing the class or the people outside, or both.

We fiddled and squirmed. The rocks seemed to have stopped for good.

"Our driver is here," Mrs. Lewis said, "even though it's not quite lunchtime. Class is dismissed for the day."

Her words, normally met with a cheer, settled over us like a damp fog. No one moved. Lara's face was bright red, and her nose quivered and sniffed. I knew how she felt. I didn't want to get beat up. Were the people outside waiting for us to spill out of the classroom? What did they plan to do next?

I tore a piece of paper out of my notebook and wrote Lara a note: "Don't worry. It's going to be ok. I'll walk to the van with you."

She reached for my hand under the table. Together, we waited for someone to make the first move.

Johan stood up. Roberto and Etienne followed.

Mrs. Lewis put her hand on each of their shoulders as they passed. "Well done, boys."

The rest of us gathered together into a tight pack outside the classroom door, then walked together to the van. Lara and I held hands as if we were kindergarteners. But I didn't care what the other kids might think.

I steeled myself for more rocks. I already knew what that felt and sounded like. But there were none.

"See you tomorrow," Mrs. Lewis said, and padlocked the door.

When we got home, Maman was napping in her room. She'd left instructions for lunch on the counter. Later that afternoon, she collapsed onto the living room sofa with a damp folded facecloth to her forehead, complaining of a raging headache. I decided to wait until after supper to tell her and Daddy what had happened at school.

Etienne and I stayed quiet while we ate our roasted chicken and our parents discussed the logistics of a trip to Masada and the Dead Sea. But as we were finishing our bowls of strawberry ice cream, Maman shared some news of her own.

"I went back to the Tiberias Hotel today. For Susanna Petersson's water aerobics class." Her tone of voice was the same one she used at the market when she didn't want to be taken for a naïve foreign woman. It matched her tight-lipped responses over most of supper and her tears of frustration when the pepper sauce she was making turned into a lumpy mess that had to be poured down the sink.

She rubbed her forehead with one hand. With the other, she poured steaming tea into my father's cup. The honey brown liquid swirled and settled while she waited for him to respond. Etienne asked to be excused, but Maman insisted he remain seated. Normally by this time I would have gotten up to clear the table and start the supper dishes. Instead, I poured myself some tea, then added milk, one drop at a time.

"Were you there all day?" my father asked. I was sure he had not missed Maman's less-than-friendly tone, yet he wasn't letting on.

"All morning."

She spooned sugar into her tea, something she only did when she was especially tired or recovering from an illness. At the second teaspoon, my father's eyes widened.

"Perhaps we need something stronger than tea," he said. "A glass of Baileys? Crème de menthe? I have a nice Porto I brought back from my observation post last week, a gift from the Italian captain ..."

Maman's spoon made a small clinking sound against the side of the flowered porcelain cup.

"Molly O'Shaughnessy was sitting there in the shade with the rest of us, in the garden next to the pool, when Patricia White came in and told us that four UN officers were killed in Beirut."

"I know. Their jeep went over a land mine." Daddy pushed his chair back from the table so that he could cross his legs. "Headquarters asked us to keep it quiet. White must have gone home and told his wife."

"Best that Molly hear it from her friend," my mother said, "rather than the military police."

"Lara's dad was killed?" I asked. It had to be a mistake.

"Lara's dad. Molly's husband. Gone." Maman put her teaspoon down. "Molly just pulled a box of animal crackers out of her beach bag and lined the cookies up on the arm of her chair, for the twins to eat. She kept saying, 'Find all the elephants, and eat them first. Then the giraffes.'"

I thought of Aileen and Liam's curly blond heads. *Two twenty-pound sacks of taters.* How Lara and I had not let go of each other's hands until the bus had reached the bottom of the hill and she was almost home.

My father went to the cupboard we used as a pantry, pulled out a glossy bottle, then brought two small glasses to the table. "We lost four men: Pat O'Shaughnessy, two Finns — Junger and Koskinen — and Wrigley, an Aussie from Melbourne — no kids."

"*Mon Dieu.*" Maman put her head in her hands.

"It was a landmine, on the side of the road. They pulled over — maybe to change a flat tire — we'll never know."

"What are we doing here?" Maman said from between her hands. "It could have been you. *Mon Dieu*, it could have been me, hearing that news today. Those little children — without a father ..."

I ran my fingers over the stitch pattern on my embroidered napkin.

"They're sending the bodies back to their countries, along with the families," my father said. "They'll be gone in a couple of days."

"All taken care of." Maman wiped her hands together. "Nice and tidy." Her mascara ran down her face in squiggly lines.

"I'm sorry you found out that way," Daddy said.

"When were you going to tell me?"

"I hadn't decided. I didn't realize you already ..."

"There are a lot of things you don't realize." She was angry now, gathering all the remaining dishes and clattering them together on a serving tray.

Etienne got up and stood in the kitchen doorway.

"I am not responsible for this disaster." My father studied the label on the bottle of liquor.

"Don't go getting yourself killed."

"Beirut is a long way from Tiberias."

"What were they doing there?" I asked.

Maman stared at me.

"They were on a three-week peacekeeping mission." Daddy took a sip of his drink. "Nothing elaborate. Just observation."

Due home on the twenty-fourth.

"You're not going there, are you?" The dripping mascara made my mother's face look like it was behind bars.

"No," my father said. "I'm not."

Maman folded her napkin into a small square.

I gathered up the rest of the dishes. "We had some trouble at school today. Someone broke into our classroom and put dog poop on the floor. Later on, they threw rocks at the roof."

"Stupid racist punks," Etienne said.

Maman folded another napkin and placed it beside the first.

"Sounds like a childish prank." My father got up from the table. "I'm going to take a walk. Care to join me?"

"I'm too tired," Maman said.

"Etienne?"

No answer.

That left me.

Walking at night was one of my favourite things to do. I liked being able to glimpse inside the neighbours' homes and see them at the table, watching TV, or reading. It was as close to them as I could get. The night air intensified the heady smells of exotic flowers, cooking spices, and diesel fumes, and the palm trees were wrapped in tiny white fairy lights that made the streets seem magical.

I looked at my father's face, then down at the messy table. I shook my head.

It took a few minutes for him to change out of his slippers into the walking shoes he kept near the door. I expected him to turn around one last time, to see if any of us had changed our minds. But he quietly laced his shoes, pushed open the door, and left.

THANKSGIVING

*Where were we heading now, and what did the future
have in store for us?*

JULES VERNE
TWENTY THOUSAND LEAGUES UNDER THE SEA

In October, I made my first Israeli friend, a girl named Efrat, who lived in our building. She showed up at our apartment one evening, while Etienne was playing a scale on his trumpet. Unlike the other girls in our neighbourhood, she had short hair — parted on the side and pushed back behind her ears, where it curled around her face. She wore pants instead of the traditional long skirts of the Orthodox community. Not waiting to be invited in, she stepped past me into the living room. "Who are you?" she asked Etienne with a throaty Hebrew accent. "Where do you come from?"

"Canada." Etienne resumed his scale.

I pointed at the maple leaf on the front of my shirt. My father had told us to sew Canadian badges on our backpacks. He'd given us stickers for our suitcases and pins for our hats and coats. Our country, he'd said, was a friend to all the nations — not like the United States, France, or Russia, who took sides.

"I am Efrat." She said she was fourteen and had lived in Israel all her life. "Born here," as if that gave her special importance.

She took in my jean shorts and T-shirt, my Mickey Mouse watch and braids. She pointed to my father's blue beret on a hook near the door and shouted over the trumpet blast, "United Nations?" She made a hippie peace sign with her fingers.

I waved at her to follow me into my bedroom.

She tried on my roller skates and ran her hand over the dozens of paperback books on my shelf. When I showed her my stamp collection, she studied each stamp as if it held a secret.

Maman knocked on my door. "You can come out now. He's finished practising." She rubbed her forehead. Etienne's trumpet playing was a quick recipe for a headache. "Come have a snack."

Efrat abandoned the stamp album on my bed and followed my mother.

When I got to the kitchen, she was already sipping a Coke. Maman offered us each a homemade date square.

"Try one," I urged Efrat, taking a big bite. "They're the best."

She shook her head no, but I could tell by the way she looked from the plate to my mouth that she wanted one. She was a bit overweight — almost twice my size — so I figured maybe she was on a special diet.

We were chatting about Israeli high school and her favourite subjects when we were interrupted by a booming male voice.

"It's my abba." My new friend grabbed her can of Coke and jumped up from her chair.

"EFRAT!" the baritone persisted.

The next day, after school, Efrat brought me up to her apartment. She wanted to practise her English so she could visit her sister in America. "New York," she said in an awed voice, as if it were some kind of dreamland.

She showed me her sister's postcards, all neatly arranged in a photo album. The Statue of Liberty, Ellis Island, Central Park. Glossy photos on one side, square Hebrew lettering in blue or black ballpoint pen on the other.

"I also have a brother. Cute, like yours." She puckered her lips and kissed the air.

Etienne the heartthrob. Why couldn't I have the same effect on my brother's friends?

"My brother is in the army." Efrat pointed to a photograph of a young man in military fatigues taped to the refrigerator door. "I will fight too." She made pretend machine-gun fire with her right arm. "For Israel."

I ran my tongue over my newly straightened teeth, checking for hints of a return to their former crookedness. There were armed Israeli soldiers on all the main streets of Tiberias, shouldering their guns like lunch boxes while they leaned against storefronts or rode the bus. Though a common sight, it was impossible for me to get used to.

"When I am eighteen, it will be my turn to serve in the IDF," Efrat said in a louder-than-usual voice. She repeated slowly and with emphasis on every syllable: "The Is-ra-el-li De-fen-se For-ce." The way she said it, as if she were speaking about royalty, made me think of Grandmaman in Montreal when she talked about the Catholic Church and its priests.

"What about Canada? How long do you serve? Here, for women, two years." She picked up my braid and started to undo it, combing it out with her fingers. "I love your hair," she said. "So long, blonde, and curly."

"We don't join unless we want to," I explained. The thought of joining the Canadian army had never entered my mind.

I caught our reflection in the gilded mirror on the dining room wall. "Who are you fighting against?" I pictured Efrat in a tank with the guys from *M*A*S*H*.

"Lebanon," she said, picking up her hairbrush. "Syria." She brushed my hair hard. "The PLO. Arafat. All the enemies of Israel."

I moved forward, breaking free of her grasp. My scalp stung from the force of her brushing. "I need to go home. I'll come back and visit as soon as I can."

"Next time, I'll make you a fancy hairstyle," she said as she walked me to the door.

When my father brought home a box of tinned and packaged food — a gift from the Canadian government to help us celebrate Thanksgiving — Efrat and I lined the contents up on the kitchen table. Tinned turkey. Cranberry sauce. Powdered potatoes and instant gravy. Imitation stuffing. Broken Oreo cookies.

"Substandard." Maman plucked the cardboard boxes of potatoes, gravy, and stuffing out of the line and put them in the garbage. "We didn't come here to eat army rations."

When she grabbed the Oreo bag, Efrat asked if she could have it. She loved sweets.

"Let me check the expiration date," Maman said. "This box may have been packed a couple of years ago."

Efrat took the bag and examined it from every angle. "This is a present to you from your country?"

"Sort of." Maman made a face as if one of us had farted.

Efrat ran her finger down the long list of Oreo ingredients.

"What are you doing?" I'd seen her scrutinize labels before, on chocolate and granola bars we'd brought from Canada, but I'd been too shy to ask why.

"Ima told me to check everything for kosher. So I eat only what God wants."

The only food I knew God was interested in was the tiny wafer the priest placed into my cupped hands in the communion line on Sunday morning. I liked the way it melted on my tongue and left a memory of honey toast behind.

"Jews have rules," Efrat said.

I wondered how many our family had broken.

"You are welcome to join us for our Thanksgiving meal."

Maman put the remaining tins into the pantry. "If your parents are willing."

Efrat's smile was polite, but her creased forehead didn't look hopeful. She set the bag of cookies on the pantry shelf next to the canned turkey and put her hand on my arm. "Come upstairs. There's something I want to show you."

Efrat's apartment was almost the same as ours, but it had cooking smells I didn't recognize and a cluttered, lived-in feeling that made our place seem like a few rooms in a hotel.

On her balcony, she'd built a palm-branch shelter for the fall feast of Sukkot. "To remember the time when my people were homeless in the desert."

We huddled inside to eat our snack of figs and dates.

"Tonight, I'll sleep here," Efrat said.

It was like being in a tree fort. Through a gap in the branches, I could see the street below, where three of the girls from our building were sitting on a bench, licking ice cream cones.

"Will your parents sleep in here with you?"

Efrat fiddled with a branch that had detached itself from the frame. "No. Just me."

I wished I could take back my question. I'd forgotten that both Efrat's parents were obese. Her mother was bedridden, the covers mounting above her like waves forming and receding under the tides of her breath. Her father was able to walk around the apartment, but only by holding onto the furniture and leaning on the wall. We could hear their deep, guttural voices from our apartment below. "EFRAT!" they would call, and she would come running.

Efrat stretched out on her back. "We leave our shelters open to the sky so we can gaze at the same stars as our ancestors."

I loved cooking and sleeping outside. When we went camping, my father showed me things, like how to make a sundial out of stones and sand, how to whittle with a penknife, and how to build a fire that could be lit with only one match. But we'd sold our tent trailer back in Yellowknife before moving away.

"Every Israeli family makes one," Efrat said. "It's easy. I can help you."

I ran down the stairs and into our apartment, eager to ask Maman if we could build a shelter of our own.

I found her in the living room with a United Nations officer in a blue beret. What was a man other than my father doing there, in the middle of the afternoon, having tea and cookies with Maman? Curious, I sat down to join them.

The man was perched on the edge of our pink velour couch, hands on his knees as if ready to spring up at any moment. While my mother poured the tea, he brushed invisible crumbs off his pant leg.

"You must be the major's daughter," he said in a heavy Scottish accent.

I pressed my lips together into a shy smile. On a recent visit to the MAC House, my father had pointed him out to me as the senior officer in charge of UN troops in Tiberias.

"As you are well aware," the man said, turning his attention back to my mother, "four peacekeepers were killed by a landmine earlier this month when they pulled their jeep over to the side of the road." He broke a digestive cookie in two and stuffed it into his mouth. "Outside Beirut."

"Molly O'Shaughnessy is a friend of mine." My mother balanced her teacup on her lap.

Guilt gnawed at my insides with its rodent-like teeth. My dad was alive, and Lara O'Shaughnessy's was dead. She'd never come back to school to say goodbye, but left almost right away for Ireland. I should have sent her a letter by now, but everything I had tried to write sounded stupid and trivial.

"We asked for volunteers to take their place in Beirut, and your husband came forward. He'll be the operations officer."

Maman set her cup on the glass coffee table. She stared at the uneaten cookie on the saucer. "When will he begin?"

"As soon as possible." The man filled the silence by eating another cookie.

"*Et nous?*" It was as though, for a moment, my mother had forgotten the man was sitting there. "Where will we live? *La guerre civile* ... the war with Israel ... *les bombardements* ... *Impossible de se trouver un appartement.*" She still had not looked up from her cup.

"You cannot follow him there. Think of the danger."

"*Je l'ai suivi jusqu'ici.*"

"We followed him all the way here," I translated.

The man stood. He did not look as tall as I remembered from when I'd first seen him at the MAC House.

"I must be on my way ... thank you for the lovely tea." He fiddled with the velcro band of his wristwatch while my mother stared at her palms as if trying to decipher her future. "I'll see myself out."

As soon as the door shut behind him, I moved next to my mother on the couch. She smoothed her hand over the velour sofa cushion, back and forth, as though petting a cat.

I ran my hand over the sofa like Maman. Part of me wanted to wipe away the news, sweep any remaining bits into the garbage. But my mind was buzzing with questions. "What will Beirut be like? Will there be any other Canadian families?"

"I don't know." Maman piled the officer's cup on top of her own. "The war wasn't part of our plan. Lebanon is a mess. Their president just got assassinated."

I felt as though someone had thrown sand in my eyes. "Why would Daddy volunteer to go into a war zone?"

"You'll have to ask him." Maman covered her face with her hands.

I made patterns in the velour. It was soft and comforting against my open palm.

"My friend Sharon will be here in a few minutes." Maman wiped her eyes. "We're going to buy a turkey for Thanksgiving dinner. Do you want to come?"

Sharon was a middle-aged Canadian woman from Toronto. She had hair dyed jet black, with a thick fringe across her forehead and a way of moving her body that made me think of soap opera stars. She was dressed in a tight-fitting pantsuit that accentuated her breasts. She and her husband, Brad, had just gotten married before moving to the Middle East on what Sharon referred to as an extended honeymoon.

At the meat market, we endured a half-hour negotiation over the price of an entire turkey, my mother flapping her ridiculous arms and tracing shapes through the air to explain that she wanted the whole thing, not just a piece. The three merchants stared at her, dumbfounded. The older one held up a blue-veined wing.

"No," my mother said. "All of it."

A single yellow tooth adorned the older merchant's bottom gum. "For you, American girls, twenty-five dolla. One hundred shekel."

Sharon and my mother both shook their heads.

"*Tish'im,*" the man countered. "Ninety."

"*Chamishim,*" Sharon said. "Fifty."

Embarrassed about the bargaining and the bad Hebrew and feeling about to vomit from the smell of raw meat, I stepped away from the stall and inspected my hair for split ends. I was thankful we had not taken Efrat along, despite our meagre language skills. Finally, my mother pulled eighty shekels — about thirty Canadian dollars — from her purse with a theatrical sigh and laid them on the bloodstained table that served as a counter. "*Ça vaut la peine.*"

The oldest of the butchers, the one who had done the bargaining, disappeared behind the stall while his two partners stared at us and our shekels on the bloodied table, slight smiles playing on their lips. A few moments later, the older man returned with a live bird hanging upside down by its talons. *"Hors de question,"* my mother said as he came toward her. *"Loh,"* she said in Hebrew, pointing at the wiggling bird and taking a few steps backwards. She drew the index finger of her right hand across her throat in a slashing motion. "Dead."

The three men laughed.

The older merchant pointed to a fly-covered carcass suspended from a hook, feathers clinging in patches to its pimpled skin. It hung there, on display in the open air, like cotton candy at a fair. Sharon laughed. "We'll take it. Eighty shekels." She pointed at the money. Then, turning to my mother, "We're in deep already. Once it's all cooked and properly basted, it will look great."

I decided I would skip the meat and eat only the vegetables.

"My cat Kissa goes crazy over turkey," Sharon said. "I can't wait to show it to him."

We carried the bird back to Sharon's apartment, its hindquarters hanging out of the plastic mesh basket my mother used for her shopping. "I brought my *Canadian Living* recipe book with me," Sharon said as we walked. "It has a great recipe for turkey stuffing with pecans and dates. I'll serve it with mashed potatoes, peas, and carrots."

"Not the ones the government sent us, I hope." My mother was limping slightly, favouring her right leg, a sign that she was tired.

"Don't be ridiculous," Sharon said.

I kept waiting for Maman to tell her friend about Daddy's news.

"We'll bring wine," Maman said when it was time for us to head back. "The German kind that Brad likes. It goes nicely with poultry."

Whenever Sharon smiled, her eyes disappeared behind the thick black fringe of her bangs. "It'll be just like home."

But that night, on the way to Brad and Sharon's, my mother realized she'd forgotten the wine. Daddy had been late getting home and it had been a scramble to get out the door. It was growing dark, and the shops were closed. "In Québec, we could buy it at any corner store," she said.

Etienne flipped his skateboard around. "I can go back and get it."

"No," my mother said. "I don't want you alone on the streets. It's not safe."

"Don't baby him," my father said.

"It's our job to protect the children." Maman wrapped her arms around her body, even though it wasn't cold.

Etienne rode his board along the sidewalk ahead of us, skipping over the cracks.

"Brad will have wine in stock." Daddy squinted at a preening bird in the high branch of a fig tree. My parents were always on the lookout for rare or exotic birds. They competed to see who would be first to spot a new species. "That might be a whiskered tern. I read that they winter here, because of the freshwater lake."

Maman stopped walking, but didn't look at the bird. "Colonel McInnis came to see me today. He told me what you've done. How could you volunteer without asking me? Why throw yourself into the war?"

My father did not slow his pace. "It's why I'm here."

"But we came with you."

He stopped and slowly turned to face her. "You'll have to go back to Canada."

"No."

Etienne had skated off the sidewalk ahead of us and onto the smooth pavement of the street, then scrambled back when a car approached.

"Stay in Israel, then. In Nahariya, on the coast." My father studied the oncoming cars, as if trying to identify their drivers.

"The countries are at war. I'll never see you."

"What will you do, then?"

Maman crossed her arms over her chest as if to shield her heart. "We're coming with you."

We walked in silence for a few minutes. The date palms that lined the main street, usually so tall and noble, trimmed to perfection by the city gardeners, looked forlorn, their branches cut or torn off by neighbourhood children to make Sukkot shelters.

"When were you planning to tell us?"

Maman's tone was accusatory but Daddy remained calm.

"I didn't want to dampen the celebration." His casual walk turned into a march. Shoulders rolled back, chest puffed out, he swung his arms back and forth like pendulums on a grandfather clock.

My mother and I fell behind. "*Tu m'as trahi*," she said to his rigid back.

Her words surprised me. In French, the phrase was an accusation of betrayal by a husband or wife.

"Brad also volunteered," my father said when we reached the end of the street. "We leave a few days after Christmas."

My mother looked at the cars passing and at the dishevelled trees. "We'd better hurry up and get to Sharon's. I said I'd help her with the dinner."

"I'm not crossing without my cat," Sharon insisted when my father, in a cautionary tone, advised us of the potential risks at the border.

"Is it worth it, Sharon?" Brad asked. His face looked peculiar because of the lack of eyebrows, recent casualties when the *mazout* stove that heated their tiny apartment blew up. I could tell he was wearing a wig.

My father sniffed his wine, then took a long drink. "We can't cross the Israeli–Lebanese border. Too much shelling. We'll need to go through Syria."

"No one ever crosses over from Israel to Syria." My mother got up from the table, gripping her linen napkin.

When the men didn't answer, she looked at me. "*Aide-moi dans la cuisine.* Gather the plates and warm them in the oven."

"UN officials cross all the time," Brad said, but my mother was already in the kitchen. I hustled to join her, relieved that it was finally time to eat. We'd had to wait an hour for Brad to come back from his patrol on the Golan and then another hour after that for the turkey to be fully cooked.

When I got to the kitchen, Maman had her elbows on the

blue tiled counter, her face in her hands. *"Les assiettes..."* She gestured toward the oven.

As I put down the stack of plates, I saw Kissa. The smoky-grey cat had squeezed his considerable body into the space between kitchen cupboard and counter. With whiskered face pressed into the golden turkey, he was licking its glowing skin. When I snapped my fingers, he looked up just long enough for me to see that he'd chewed a chunk of meat off the right turkey breast.

"Kissa!" I whispered. I put my body between the cat and my mother. I wanted to dislodge him without her noticing, to spare her this final defeat. But the cat kept licking.

"Qu'est ce que tu fais?" she asked just as the cat lifted his head, a piece of white meat dangling from his left whisker.

My mother yanked on his tail, and the cat squealed and scrambled, then jumped to the floor, my mother kicking the air behind him.

Back at the table, she and I watched the men and Etienne spear large pieces of turkey with their forks. They were still talking about the move to Lebanon. I wondered if Brad's eyebrows would ever grow back, or if he'd have to stay that way forever.

Sharon set down her lipstick-smeared wine glass. "We have to find a way to smuggle Kissa out of Israel. After leaving my daughter in Canada, I can't handle any more goodbyes." She turned glassy eyes on her husband. "It's my first Thanksgiving without her."

"We should go around the table and say what we're thankful for," Brad said. "That's what I always did at home with my kids."

"Tat's an English ting," Maman said. Her accent thickened whenever she drank wine, and she lost the ability to pronounce the "th." "It's not part of our French-Canadian traditions."

"What about dessert?" Etienne asked.

Sharon jumped up from the table. "I made an apple pie."

We shovelled it in as if it were our last meal. No one said anything about being thankful.

On the walk home, close to midnight, we were careful to skirt the metal dumpsters where Tiberias's army of cats held court and from which they leaped out onto the sidewalk as if they owned the city. They must have started out as house pets, Daddy said, and turned feral over time.

We held our bloated bellies as we walked. By the time we got to our street, my tummy was a hard, round ball.

"We'll have to consult the military doctor." Maman loosened the belt around her dress. "We may have gotten food poisoning."

"We would have been better off eating the government supplies." My father's arms swung into marching mode. "We could have washed them down with an extra old bottle of Merlot or Cabernet Sauvignon. Or one of the Israeli wines I brought home last week."

"You have no idea how much work went into making you that feast," my mother snapped.

Etienne pressed his skateboard against his belly and groaned. "I think I'm going to die."

"Don't say that," Maman said. "Don't ever say that."

"Maman," Etienne said, "you're starting to sound as hysterical as Sharon."

When we reached our apartment building, a crowd of men, women, and children were dancing and singing in the front parking lot. One man played an accordion while another beat on a tambourine. Its colourful ribbons trailed behind him.

"So much for a peaceful night's sleep," my father said.

In spite of my bellyache, I was drawn to the festivities. I recognized many of our neighbours' faces, including several girls my age flushed from spinning and twirling their arms. It was a summery night, warm with no breeze. The men were stepping backwards to form a wide circle while the women formed their own circle further down the road. Part of me wanted to hold hands with my family, to dance with my parents and Etienne — something I'd never done before — but since I'd undone my jeans, I had to hold my T-shirt down with one hand to cover my protruding belly.

I looked for an opening in the circles, but no one made room for us. We walked between parked cars to reach the apartment building doors.

"I'm sure they'll invite us." I looked back over my shoulder, hoping to see a friendly wave from one of our neighbours.

"Even if they did, I'm in too much pain to dance," Maman said.

"Don't you want to fit in?" I asked. "We live in the same

building with all these people, but the only family we know is Efrat's."

Last year, Mrs. Nouger had insisted that our grade six class be inclusive. It was her favourite word. We'd made a banner declaring "We celebrate our differences" and draped it above the classroom door. It was a cutout of miniature people in every shade of skin colour. They were dressed in their countries' traditional outfits, with their national flags pinned to their chests, holding hands and smiling.

"Why can't they include us?" I asked.

"We won't be here much longer." Etienne looked over to the building next to ours, where Johan lived, but the lights in the Nilssons' apartment were all turned off. "Only a couple more months."

It was hard to fall asleep with the street music and the bellyache. I lay in bed wondering what Beirut would be like.

"We're moving to Lebanon," I told Efrat the next day. She'd spread her stationery collection on the kitchen table and was letting me choose my favourite sheet. I picked up a white one edged in blue, with Snoopy on the roof of his doghouse. I could use it to write a letter to Lara.

Efrat looked at me as if I'd spoken Mandarin or Swedish. Her hands smoothed out a crease in a lined sheet with a black-and-white Pierrot clown in the corner. She looked over to her parents' bedroom. The door was wedged open with a slipper. "You'll be living with my enemies." Her eyes were as round and sad as the clown's. "We've been at war with Lebanon all my life."

It hadn't been my decision. I knew nothing about Beirut. I didn't even want to go there. But I still felt like a traitor.

"We're not leaving until after Christmas," I said. "You can help me decorate our tree."

Efrat tidied her sheets into a pile. "Will you hang things on the lime tree on your balcony?"

"The Canadian government sent us a fake fir tree," I said. "In a box."

Efrat slipped each piece of stationery into its protective covering. At the front of the binder were the sheets I'd given her: a barefoot Ziggy with his little white dog, the Human Beans of Beanville, and a bright yellow paper with Garfield at the top, frowning over a bowl of lasagna.

"We'll string the tree with popcorn garlands and gingerbread men. It'll be fun," I said, even though my heart wasn't in it.

Efrat tucked her binder under her arm. "Please don't send me a letter from Lebanon. It could cause problems for my family." She turned her sad Pierrot eyes on me again. "Not even a postcard."

She didn't mention the Sukkot shelter again, but I didn't feel like building it any more. I didn't want to sleep on the balcony; it felt too exposed, too vulnerable, where neighbours or people on the street could watch me while I slept. There was always the possibility of scorpions and the cockroaches we'd seen in Tiberias's cafés. And the danger of rats and other nocturnal predators. It was better to stay hidden inside.

My parents at the Tiberias Hotel (Sea of Galilee in the background),
September 1982.

~

TAKING
POSSESSION

~

Calvin: Dad, how do people make babies?
Dad: Most people just go to Sears, buy the kit, and follow
the assembly instructions.
Calvin: I came from Sears??
Dad: No. You were a blue light special at K-mart. Almost
as good, and a lot cheaper.

BILL WATTERSON, *CALVIN AND HOBBES*

A few days after Thanksgiving, Maman and I walked to Sharon and Brad's apartment. "We'll discuss the move with Sharon," Maman said on the way, "and come up with a plan."

She avoided saying the name of the city that was to be our next home. As if Beirut had become a dirty word.

But once we reached her, Sharon had other preoccupations. "Brad and I want to have a baby."

My mother's eyebrows rose until they were almost touching her hairline. *Translation: My daughter must leave the room before we discuss things that are too adult for her twelve-year-old virgin ears.*

When Sharon bobbed her head it made the skin on her neck jiggle. "Do you like to read *Seventeen?*" Her voice rose an octave higher than usual. "I bought the latest issue for when my daughter, Patsy Ann, comes to visit at Christmas." She pulled a slim magazine from the bookshelf behind the sofa and thrust it into my hands. "Why don't you lie on the guest bed while you flip through it?"

I followed Sharon into the spare room, assessing the distance to the living room and how easy it would be to overhear the conversation.

"Do you miss her?" I asked.

"She loves Collingwood. It's the best school in Vancouver — maybe even in Canada. I could never have afforded it, but the government is paying. You could have gone there too, you know." She dabbed at her eyes, smudging the layers of mascara, blue eye shadow, and foundation.

I nodded as if I'd been given the choice. But I couldn't imagine living without Maman and Daddy. If they had considered leaving Etienne and me at boarding school in Canada while they went to the Middle East for a year, they'd never told us.

Sharon shut the door behind her, with the promise to bring me a lemonade.

The residential neighbourhood was quiet. If I sat still and turned my head toward the door, I could hear my mother and Sharon perfectly.

"Every marriage needs a child," Sharon said. "A baby will be a symbol of our love and unity. A baby will make us a family."

"You and Brad are already a family," Maman said. "How old is he, anyway?"

"Fifty in November."

"Sharon, he'll be an old man by the time ..."

"But I want to start over with him. I want to do it right this time. Patsy Ann is almost all grown up, and Brad will never get his boys back from their mother's grip. This is our chance."

"But you're my age. Forty is too old to start over."

"If it doesn't work, we can always adopt. I'm sure there are all kinds of unwanted babies around here." Sharon's voice was climbing an octave again. "Apparently, if you know the right people, you can get a baby in Syria or Lebanon. From the camps."

"A Palestinian baby?" Maman's voice fell to a whisper. I couldn't hear the rest, until her voice rose again: "Sharon, this isn't like buying a Turkish carpet to bring back to Canada. You can't just ..."

"I know, I know. Brad is looking into it."

"Maybe you should try for your own."

"It's risky. And I don't want to be burdened with a handi-capped child. But I want this so badly."

Sharon's cat, Kissa, jumped onto the bed. It blinked, then circled around me, tickling my bare legs with its broom-like tail. When it started to purr, I poked it to make it stop. I didn't want anything to prevent me from overhearing the conversation in the other room.

"Adoption saves lives," Sharon said. The cat curled into a ball beside me, its fat hind end squarely on the magazine. "The mothers are Muslim girls who get pregnant before marriage. They have no choice but to give up their babies. And a child will make Brad feel young again."

"But without children, the two of you are so free," Maman said.

Either she thought the walls were made of brick or she'd forgotten about me. I felt as small and inconsequential as the pink-and-black gecko on the windowsill. Through its translucent skin I could see the frantic pulse of veins in its belly. Had its lidless eyes seen the sleeping cat?

"They say there are twelve Palestinian camps in Southern Lebanon," Sharon continued. The rattle of teacups startled the gecko. He slipped into a crack between the window casing and the wall. "There's got to be a baby in one of them for me."

Kissa's ears twitched at the click of the pillbox my mother kept in her purse for ready access to headache medication. "Is that why Brad volunteered for Beirut?"

"We thought it might increase our chances if we were closer to the camps."

Sharon stopped talking for a while. She must have remembered my lemonade and gone to the kitchen to make it. I tugged on the magazine to get it out from under Kissa's large body, but the cat refused to budge. I gave up and wandered out to join Maman.

"*J'ai tout entendu*," I whispered. I heard everything.

Maman's hands fluttered up to her hairpins and then to her earrings, as if to check that she was intact. "I've tried to shield you for as long as I could. But Beirut will be quite an education."

I wasn't sure what to make of this dubious open door into the adult world. But when Sharon came back with drinks and an elaborate nail polish kit, I tucked my feet under me on the couch.

"She can stay," Maman said, before Sharon could intervene. I smiled into my lemonade.

"It's unnatural for a newlywed couple to be separated," Sharon complained to my mother as we were leaving.

"But it's what we're here for. Our husbands are observers."

"I want him to observe me." Sharon ran her hand over her form-fitting dress.

Maman laughed. I wondered why Sharon was so made up, since her husband was away from home. With her dyed and permed hair and heavy makeup, she looked like an exotic bird in search of a place to land.

Her polka-dot dress with its scooped front and row of tiny buttons reminded me of the dress Maman had worn a few weeks back. Etienne and I had come home early from movie night at the MAC House only to find the front door of our apartment locked.

Etienne banged on the door. "I know Maman and Daddy are inside. They would never leave this many lights on for nothing."

When Maman opened the door, she was holding the front of her dress closed with one hand.

"The couch is taken!" my father called from the living room.

Maman had a faraway look and a funny smile on her face. "You're home," she said. The three of us stood in a semicircle, unsure what to do or say.

"I'm hungry." It was Etienne's most frequent contribution.

I slipped off to my room, making a wide circle around the couch so I wouldn't have to face my father, even though he'd been away for the last ten days.

"Imagine getting married and moving to the Middle East," my mother said the morning after our conversation with Sharon.

My father peered at her from behind the *Jerusalem Post*. "Imagine being married four times."

Or taking your family into a war zone. I didn't dare say it aloud.

"Her hair isn't really black," Etienne said. "I can tell. Hair doesn't come in that shade unless you're an Indian."

"An Aboriginal." Maman opened the kitchen window, letting in a cool breeze and the mingled sounds of honking cars and mewling cats. In the valley below, a rooster crowed.

"Could we adopt a cat?" I asked. "Like Brad and Sharon?"

My mother spread the butter to the edges of her toast. Was she thinking about Mr. Schumann, Etienne's hamster, left behind in Yellowknife? The dog we could never get because we moved so often? "They're filthy," she said. "Disease carriers. We've been warned not to touch them."

But I wasn't ready to give up. "That's what you say about the fruit and vegetables and the meat in the market, but you buy them anyway. We could wash the cat. We could ..."

"We're not here for much longer."

Etienne jumped in. "We still have two months to go. And we could bring the cat with us when we leave. The Nilssons have a cat. And so do the Herreras."

"We'll see." These days, it was Maman's answer to everything.

Sharon came over a week later. Her thick black bangs hung low over her eyes like a curtain. "Brad met a doctor who works for Oxfam. He says there's a convent near the Sabra and Shatila camps." She helped me unpack the fruit from our mesh shopping bags and place it on the counter. "The nuns take in the unwed girls. As soon as the babies are viable, the women are given a c-section and returned to their families."

"What about the scar?" Maman filled the sink with water and squirted in some ammonia. I selected one of our kitchen knives and made an incision into the fleshy skin of a mango.

"They tell the family it was appendicitis." Sharon wiped her palms together several times, then inspected her manicured fingernails. "It's all very neatly done. The young woman is saved from being murdered by her father and brothers, and the baby's life is spared.

"We decided we'd prefer a boy," she continued. "Brad is still so heartsick about losing his sons. And Vancouver and

Toronto are worlds apart. He's pretty sure he'll never get to see them. His ex-wife needs to come to terms with the fact that he doesn't love her anymore. She's incredibly vindictive. She refuses even to say my name. She calls me 'her' or 'that woman.'" Sharon spat out the words.

This was better than the afternoon soap operas Maman had let me watch in Canada when I was too sick to go to school.

She put her hand on Sharon's arm. "You're squeezing the strawberries too hard. And I don't take the stem off until after I've soaked them in the ammonia solution. That way, they don't leave a bad taste in your mouth."

Etienne cleared his throat. He was leaning against the kitchen door frame with his arms behind his back, grinning. "I've got something to show you."

It was a small orange cat with eyes the colour of the Sea of Galilee. It trembled against Etienne's chest when I ran my hand along its back.

"It's just a baby," Sharon cooed.

"Too little to be on its own." My mother looked disapprovingly at Etienne. "Where did you find it?"

"In the parking lot, curled up next to the Peugeot's back tire. I stayed with it for a long time to see if another cat might come by to claim it, but none did."

Sharon poured milk into her palm and held it out to the kitten, who lapped it up eagerly. I copied her example.

When the milk was gone, the cat continued to lick my palm. Its tongue was rough, as if embedded with tiny pebbles. Purring loudly, the kitten climbed my shirt up to my shoulder and sucked on my earlobe.

"Look what you've done," my mother said to Sharon. "Next they'll ask me if it can stay."

"And of course you will say yes."

"Please," Etienne said. "It would be so much fun."

Say yes say yes say yes say yes.

My mother looked at Sharon. "I suppose we can give it a try."

"Yes!" Etienne and I cheered at the same time, startling the kitten. I could feel its tiny heart battering against its ribcage.

"We all need something to love." Sharon sat beside me on the sofa so that we could both pet the kitten. "When I see you in Beirut, this cat will have doubled in size. It'll be fat with love."

"You mean you're leaving soon?" my mother asked.

"In three weeks. We're going to take a holiday in Damascus on the way. I'm ready for a change."

"I'll miss you," Maman said. "But you can show me around Beirut when I get there."

"Can I open a can of tuna?" Etienne asked.

"Sure," my mother said. "Share the love, as Sharon says. But then we'll have to find a way to give that cat a bath."

"There's another reason I want to go to Damascus. There's a British doctor there I want to see — an OB-GYN who works with Doctors Without Borders." Sharon's hands fluttered to her face. She didn't seem concerned about kitten germs. "I wasn't going to say anything yet, but ... I think I may have good news." She put one hand on her lower abdomen. "I'm late."

Late for what? I was even more curious when Etienne's face went bright red. He whisked the cat out of the living room.

"Well." Maman pressed her hands together in prayer against her chest. "Congratulations."

"I can't let myself get too excited yet." Sharon smiled, and her eyes disappeared behind her bangs. "But I'm hopeful."

By the time Daddy came back from his week on observation post, the kitten had become part of our family.

"She's a ball of love," I told Daddy when she introduced herself by rubbing against his leg.

"She's gone a long way toward making the apartment feel like a home." Maman's comment followed so quickly after mine that it sounded as though she'd rehearsed it. With an argument like that, Daddy couldn't refuse.

He reached down to pet her. "What do you call her?"

"Minou." We'd been debating, unable to decide, and had settled on the French word for kitten. The name had stuck.

"Sharon is pregnant," Maman blurted.

Daddy stooped down and brought the kitten to his chest. "Now Brad won't have to buy a baby to make her happy."

"Don't be ridiculous. You're making the adoption idea sound illegal."

"It is," Daddy answered over the kitten's purr. "Highly. And I doubt that Brad has calculated the risks."

A few weeks later, I came into the living room with Minou in my arms. My mother was sitting in the middle of the sofa, cradling the telephone. "Sharon had a miscarriage," she said when I sat across from her.

"What's that?" I took a bite of the peanut butter and banana sandwich she'd made me for lunch. With Daddy away so much, Maman had taken to confiding in me, discussing topics she would otherwise have reserved for him. Part of me enjoyed the attention, but the information she shared was an unwelcome weight, like a heavy suitcase I needed to carry.

"She was pregnant, but the baby died. Sharon says she hemorrhaged — bled so much she lost consciousness."

I studied my sandwich: the moonlike craters of the bread, the sandy colour of the crust, darker brown near the edges.

"Brad had to take her to the Poriya Medical Centre. But the good news is that there's a doctor who knows where they can get a baby. Sharon says he's working on it."

I imagined a sandwich board at the entrance to the market where Maman and I went every second day to buy our vegetables, eggs, and meat. In neat black letters in both Hebrew and English would be the words *Jaffa oranges, pomegranates, and babies for sale.*

"Where will he get it?" I offered Minou a piece of my sandwich, but she sniffed it and turned away.

"There are over a million Palestinians in the Lebanese camps," Maman said.

I checked over my shoulder to make sure Etienne wasn't behind us, in the kitchen. I didn't want him listening in on the conversation about blood and babies and then snickering about it later.

"Didn't Daddy say that was illegal?"

"The war has blurred a lot of those lines." Maman massaged the bulging green vein that ran from the knuckle of her middle finger all the way to her wrist joint. "Brad and Sharon plan to arrive in Beirut in early December, a month before us."

I knew Maman was still mad at my dad for volunteering to move to Beirut without consulting her. I could hear them arguing about it at night. My middle tightened into a cramp. Maybe the ulcer was coming back. Right after Christmas we were leaving Tiberias for a city in the middle of a war. Maman had already started packing the nonessentials in the kitchen.

"Is it very dangerous?" I hated to ask, but I needed to know.

Maman examined her chipped nails. "I refuse to go back to Canada without your father. I don't want to be separated again."

Keeping one hand on my churning gut, I reached to scratch my ankle with the other. It burned as much as it had when I'd stepped into a hornets' nest while raspberry picking the summer before.

"Maman," I said, "look at this." What had been an itchy red spot earlier that morning had now spread into a full-blown rash.

"Oh, no." Maman lifted her right ankle to the couch. "I've got the same thing. It's painful, too."

We had almost identical circular patches of blistering lesions.

Maman went to our small bookshelf and pulled out the *Encyclopedia of Family Health*, which was almost as thick as the atlas. She flipped to the index at the back, then pulled the book open to a series of colour photographs. She compared my ankle to the photos.

"Ringworm! I should have known." She grabbed the sleeping kitten by the scruff of its neck and carried it into the kitchen.

"What are you doing?" I eyed the open window, worried that Maman might pitch our pet down to its death. But she opened the storage room door and put it inside.

"We'll have to get rid of it."

"How can you be sure it's the cat's fault?" I didn't want Maman to be right, even though I knew she was. The appearance of the spots coincided too neatly with the adoption of the cat. "Sharon never mentioned this."

Maman washed her hands at the sink, then reached for mine. "We'll have to wash all the furniture and the bed linens. What a fiasco."

The kitten mewed and scratched at the closed door.

"She'll have to go back to the dumpster."

"But she could die."

"It was a stupid idea. I shouldn't have let myself get talked into it."

"I'm sure we can get rid of the infection. We haven't even seen a doctor. Please." I put my hand on the storage room door.

"No." Maman shot me her 'don't mess with me' look. "I said we'd give it a try, and it hasn't worked."

I felt hollowed out.

"It was just a trial run." Maman's voice softened when she saw my quivering lip. "We hadn't even settled on a name."

"Her name is Minou." I couldn't believe my mother could switch allegiances so quickly. "She's part of the family."

"They don't like letting people cross the land borders out of Israel. The only people who are given special permission are diplomats and United Nations personnel. Taking an animal across is strictly forbidden. We would have had to smuggle her. I don't know what I was thinking." My mother put the cat's bowls in the sink and poured bleach into them. "We have to get rid of that cat. Too many risks involved."

But there were riskier things.

GETAWAY

"Monsieur is going to leave home?"
"Yes," returned Phileas Fogg, "We are going round the world."
JULES VERNE
AROUND THE WORLD IN 80 DAYS

My mother set my father's plate of stewed lamb in front of him. "Last winter, when we talked about moving here, you said we'd take the kids all over the Middle East." She handed my brother his plate. "But we've been here three months and we've never left Tiberias."

"I thought you liked it here." Daddy popped an olive into his mouth.

"I want to go on a trip. One of the weeks when you're not on the Golan. See some of the sights." Maman looked out the window as if hoping to catch a glimpse of something touristic on the horizon. "Jordan, Syria, and Egypt are all within driving distance."

"You told us we'd get to see the pyramids," Etienne said.

I liked the idea of missing school.

"Things have heated up." Daddy added pepper to his meal while the rest of us waited for what he might say next. "There's more work than I thought."

Maman still hadn't touched her food. "But you promised."

"That was last winter, when things were peaceful. I had no way of knowing that Israel would invade Lebanon."

Maman skewered a piece of lamb with her fork and moved it around her plate. "If you're too busy, I'll have to go without you."

"Too dangerous. Women don't travel alone in the Middle East."

"I'll have Etienne. He's fourteen now."

My brother's face lit up, but no more was said until my father had finished eating. He laid his fork and knife across his empty plate and pushed his chair back from the table. "You're forcing my hand."

"Then come with us."

"I've made commitments."

"Indeed you have." My mother stacked her full plate of food over my father's empty one and cleared the space in front of him. She turned her back to us while she scraped her supper into the garbage. "But touring Beirut with the family wasn't what I had in mind."

Mention of our upcoming move to Lebanon soured my stomach like a piece of undercooked meat. For Maman, it deepened the wrinkle between her eyes and accentuated her limp.

My father cleaned his teeth with a toothpick. When he was finished, he and Etienne left the messy table for Maman and me to clear.

She washed and I dried and put away, just as we'd done each night for the past four years, since I'd been old enough to meet her standards of cleanliness. But once the counters were clean and the sink disinfected — my usual cue to leave — she lifted the electric coils on the stovetop and removed the grey drip pans underneath. She scrubbed the metal with steel wool and didn't stop until even the most persistent stain was gone.

When she headed to the bathroom to run hot water into the tub, I flipped through the *National Geographic Family Atlas* we'd brought with us until I found the map of Israel and its surrounding countries. I ran my finger over the boundary lines, wondering where we might go on our vacation. South to Egypt. West to the Mediterranean. East to Jordan.

I wasn't sure I wanted to leave our apartment. I felt funny, as if the sunstroke symptoms I'd had on our visit to Jerusalem were coming back, with the addition of a dull throb at the base of my spine and in my belly. The ring of pain around my middle circled a knot of anxiety deep in my gut. To top it off, something was wrong with me — brown stuff kept staining the front of my underwear, coming out the wrong place. I put a pillow between my knees, pressed it to my body and escaped into *The Lord of the Rings* and Frodo's brave departure from his home in the Shire. Hours later, I fell asleep to the back-and-forth volley of my parents' argument: my father's low, controlled murmur and my mother's higher pitched resistance.

They were still at it before my father left for work the next day.

"I've decided to take the children to Damascus," Maman gripped the hairbrush, ready to braid my hair for school, "on Friday." She must have been rehearsing this moment, steeling herself for it all night. "With Brad and Sharon." All I knew about Damascus was that it was behind the hills on the other side of Lake Tiberias. I liked the sound of it in French: *Damas*, with its two soft, dreamy vowels.

My father polished the toes of his leather shoes with a paper napkin. "It's a dangerous city."

Etienne looked up from his cereal. "What's the worst that could happen? Are you worried we might get kidnapped, like the Americans in Iran?"

My arms broke out in goosebumps. After four hundred and forty-four days of captivity, the fifty-two American diplomats and citizens had finally been released the winter I was in grade five. We'd done a unit on it in social studies. "Could that happen to us?" I looked from my father in his impeccably clean and pressed khaki uniform to my mother, dressed in bathrobe and slippers, her hair going every which way.

She tossed her head as if to shake off unwanted thoughts. "If we gave in to our fears, we'd never go anywhere." She brushed my hair with strong, smooth strokes, just as she'd been doing for me every morning since I could remember. "We'd still be tucked away on some army base in Canada."

"Why are you so bent on leaving?" My father adjusted his blue beret in the hall mirror.

When she reached for the hair elastic on the counter, Maman's hand trembled a bit. "I could use a break."

Daddy looked at his watch. He was never late. "I'll be home for dinner at six." With a quick kiss to Maman, he was out the door. His footsteps echoed on the cement stairs.

Maman's deep exhale blew warm air into my ear. "It will be fun." She wound the loose end of my hair into a ringlet. "We'll sleep in a hotel, eat in restaurants, and go shopping."

Etienne drank the leftover milk in his bowl. "Shopping?" He scrunched his nose over his milk moustache.

"Not in a mall. In an outdoor market." My mother started in on the second braid. "I want to take you to the gold souk. It will be our little adventure." Her fingers moved swiftly through my hair. "It's only about a hundred kilometres from here to Damascus. It's the border crossing that's the tricky part."

Etienne put his empty bowl on the counter next to the stack of dirty dishes and left the room. I resented him for leaving it for me and Maman to clean up later, even though that's how it had always been in our family. This wasn't the time to bring up old battles. Our family needed to stick together, not split apart into factions.

Once my braids were finished, I followed Maman out to the balcony, where she retrieved a dishrag from the clothesline. "I deserve a holiday." She pointed at the sky. "Yesterday, our upstairs neighbour emptied her dustpan over my clothesline of freshly laundered whites."

"But what if ..."

"We'll be fine. I've been to Damascus before, when you were little and Daddy was working for the UN. It's time we explored a bit."

I was getting my books ready for school when Maman came into my bedroom. When I saw her holding something white and pink in her hand, my face flushed with humiliation. It was my bunched up underwear.

"I found this in the bottom of the bin when I emptied the bathroom garbage."

I bent over my book bag to hide my face. "I had a little accident."

She crouched beside me. "Tell me about it." Her eyes were wide, as if something good were happening instead of some weird tropical disease that was affecting me down there.

"I must be sick." Whatever it was, I didn't want to talk about it. I hid my face in a book while Maman examined the stain.

"This is menstrual blood." She threw her arms around me and burst into tears. "*Tu es devenue une femme.*"

I didn't want to be a woman. I missed being flat-chested and small. Things were going too fast. I'd forgotten our strange talk, months back, in Yellowknife, and my mother's cryptic explanation of a diagram in an anatomy book.

"Promise you won't tell Daddy. Or Etienne."

"It will be our secret." She still had that happy, proud face, like I'd won first prize in a competition. "No matter what other women tell you, this isn't a curse. It's a blessing."

I looked at my desk, my closet, the ceiling. "What do you mean?"

"It's wonderful. Your body is ready to conceive and bear a child. In some parts of the Middle East, a girl's first period marks her as being ready for marriage."

My cheeks and ears burned. How could this one thing make such a difference? I didn't like the smell my body gave off. It reminded me of the worm stink on Canadian sidewalks after a hard rain. I stretched out on my bed. "My back hurts."

"Cramps are normal. I'll get you a hot water bottle and a Tylenol." She bustled out of my bedroom, still clutching my underwear.

My body felt hijacked by the pain. "Can I stay home from school if it stays this bad?"

"Sure," Maman answered from the bathroom. "You can help me get ready for our trip." She let the water run in the sink.

Maybe I'd be too sick to go.

After lying on my bed for an hour with the hot water bottle nestled against my stomach, I went into the kitchen for a glass of juice. On the table were four passports and a large stack of paper money — not Israeli shekels but American dollars.

"Where did all this come from? Do you keep it in a drawer somewhere?" I wondered what other secrets my parents had tucked away.

My mother divided the bills into piles of ones, fives, tens, twenties, and hundreds. "I keep it in case of emergency since Daddy is gone so much."

I helped her organize each stack so that the numbers faced the same way.

"Once we cross over," she flicked a piece of chipped nail polish onto the table, then brushed it onto the floor, "we can't even say the name of Israel out loud. We must pretend as if this country doesn't exist."

I flipped through the passports for Israel. Etienne had his own, with his picture and date of birth, but I didn't. My name and photo were fixed to a page in my mother's passport, as if I were an extension of her and not my own person. This had caused all kinds of complications when we'd flown in from Montreal. The Israeli customs officials had questioned me about my age and demanded to know why I didn't have my own documents.

I put the two passports for Israel back onto the table, next to the other set we used for Arabic speaking countries. "What will we do with these?"

"We'll hide them in the suitcase — maybe in my toiletries bag."

In Magnum P.I.'s undercover operations on TV, sexy Tom Selleck had his two Dobermans, Zeus and Apollo, a fast getaway car, and a helicopter, with Higgins to help get him out of trouble. But my mother, brother, and I would be on our own in our tiny Peugeot.

A wave of cramps rippled through my lower back. I pushed back the legs of the metal kitchen chair and leaned my head against the melamine table. "I think I need to lie down."

In the bathroom, I hid my used sanitary pad in an empty toilet roll, then wadded it up with paper to camouflage it.

On the morning of our departure, as Maman had predicted, the cramps were gone, but my bloated abdomen made my jeans too tight.

"How do I look?" Maman twirled in front of the fridge and stove in our tiny apartment kitchen. "The leather is incredibly soft. *Peau de chamois*. Lined with silk. *Une petite extravagance*." She waited for my father to comment on her new pants, but he barely smiled.

"They're nice, Maman," I said, even though the brown colour made me think of something else, unmentionable in the kitchen.

It seemed enough to satisfy her. "We'll leave right after breakfast."

We stood next to the Peugeot in the parking lot of our apartment building, our bags at our feet.

Daddy stood next to his UN vehicle, briefcase in hand. "It's not too late to change your mind."

"*À dimanche*." Maman stepped forward to give him a kiss.

When it was my turn to kiss him goodbye, he squeezed my shoulders and ran his hand over my braided head. The extra attention bothered me. Had Maman betrayed my secret?

"Don't stray too far from the Damascus MAC House," Daddy said. "Let the steward know where you plan to be and how long you'll be gone. Carry your passports at all times."

Maman's face looked like she'd just scrubbed it in a hot shower. "We'll be with Brad and Sharon most of the time."

Daddy climbed into the UN jeep and we got into the Peugeot. If this had been my father's plan, he would have produced a map of Israel and the surrounding Middle Eastern nations, with our driving route highlighted in yellow. My mother had a few notes written on a scrap of paper, to be used in case we got separated from the Windsors and had to find our own way.

I felt alone in the back seat.

"Our neighbours would never believe us if they knew where we were heading," Maman said as we drove down our street. "We're so lucky. No Israeli is ever granted permission to enter Syria."

When we got to Sharon's house, Brad ran out to meet us. His wig had slipped. The bangs were crooked, and the hairpiece covered half his right ear. It was hard to take him seriously, but his face was as grey as the sidewalk. "I need Etienne's help to carry Kissa. We crushed two sleeping pills into his wet food and now he's out cold."

Between the two of them, Etienne and Brad stuffed the drugged and sleeping cat under the back seat of the Windsors' brown Mercedes.

"He might never wake up!" Sharon said. "Maybe we gave him too much."

Maman put a reassuring arm around her. She was like a sturdy tree, providing a branch for her flighty friend. But when the two of them hugged, I saw that instead of her usual neutral tones, my mother's nails were painted hot pink — the same shade as Sharon's.

Brad heaved the last suitcase and shut the trunk. "If the

Syrians find him, they could seize our passports and blacklist us. Or detain us in some stink-hole prison cell."

My shoulders and neck tensed up. I was terrified of getting caught.

But Maman was determined not to let anything spoil our fun. "Say *shalom* to Israel."

We drove an hour north to the border, with our small car in front.

The Peugeot climbed the hills in fits and starts, threatening to stall each time my mother tried to put it into higher gear. Normally, Maman would complain. But this day, in spite of the climb, she held back. "*Pas de problème,*" she said, slamming her foot on the clutch. I tried to locate our apartment complex in the valley below, but I couldn't distinguish one building from another. Minou was out there somewhere, fending for herself on a dusty Tiberias street.

I knew we were almost at the border when we reached a row of tanks. A barbed-wire fence lined both sides of the road. We pressed on.

"Cool." Etienne leaned out the window to get a better look. "These guys mean business."

But this wasn't *M*A*S*H* or *Rambo*. We came to a roadblock.

"Let me do the talking," Maman said. "Only answer if spoken to."

A soldier in army fatigues, machine gun in hand, took a few steps toward our car. He bent to look through the open window and take the documents Maman held out. Dark, curly chest hairs peeped over the collar of his khaki uniform.

With a hand motion and an Arabic command, he ordered us to exit the car.

We huddled in a group with Brad and Sharon. It was cooler here than in the valley. A sharp wind ripped through my sweatshirt.

We were surrounded by military vehicles of all sizes: tanks, trucks, pick-ups with canvas bed covers and cars with military flags and insignia. Soldiers swarmed like the deer flies that plagued Yellowknife in July.

The Syrian soldiers looked like the Israeli Defense Forces except that their berets were burgundy and their uniforms solid green instead of camouflage coloured. Each soldier had a weapon slung across his chest and attached to his belt. But unlike the Israeli army, they were all male — not a woman among them.

"Name?" the hairy border guard barked at Sharon.

Her voice came out high and wobbly, as if balanced on stiletto heels.

He had her passport open at the picture page. His eyes narrowed, and his voice grew louder. "Sha-RON," he pronounced her name like the Israeli defense minister, Ariel Sharon.

A soldier with a pencil-thin moustache and a round belly that jiggled when he walked came to stand next to him. He had two more bars on his shoulder — the mark of a senior officer. He flipped through the other four passports as if they were tabloids, hardly worth his time.

"No," Sharon insisted. "The accent is on the first syllable: Shaaaaron."

The senior guard shook his head. His moustache trembled. Something gooey was stuck to the bottom whiskers. A piece of scrambled egg, I thought, or yogurt.

"Over there." He pointed his machine gun at the edge of the platform. "Shoes. Off."

Sharon slipped out of her sandals. Moustache Soldier grunted, jutted his chin forward, and extended his hand, palm up. "Give me."

When Sharon bent over to pick them up, he stared at her breasts spilling out of her red lace bra. He smirked as she handed the shoes to him, then turned them around in his hand. "Scrape off," he said, and threw the sandals back to Sharon. She tried to catch them, but missed.

My mother bent her knee, one hand on her blouse to keep it pressed to her chest, then handed the shoe to Etienne. She pointed at the Hebrew writing stamped onto the sandal's rubber sole. "Use your knife."

He dug into his pocket, pulled out the Swiss army knife he always carried and selected a thick blade. The soldiers watched my brother as if he might turn his small weapon against them.

"We search car," the hairy guard said.

Kissa.

But he began with our Peugeot.

Would he dare to search my mother's toiletry bag? What if he found my supply of pads? What if he confiscated our passports back into Israel?

At dinner parties, one of Maman's favourite stories to tell was about the spring of 1977, when she'd travelled from

Quebec City to Tel Aviv to visit my father on one of his extended peacekeeping missions. At the airport, the Israeli airline authorities had suspected her of being a spy. "They searched me *everywhere*." She'd gesture wildly with her hands the way she did when she spoke in French. "They examined everything in my suitcase. I hadn't seen my husband in months. What do you think I had in there?" This question always elicited giggles from her female listeners. "Once they'd held up every last piece of clothing, they tore out the suitcase lining and poked around some more."

"You three!" Moustache Soldier motioned for Maman, Etienne, and me to follow him into the cement bunker. Maman walked behind him as if he were a maître d' in a fancy restaurant, showing her to her table. If she noticed the bulgy, purple, and pulsing veins on the side of Brad's neck when she passed him, she gave no indication.

We sat in a windowless corner where we couldn't see our friends on the platform.

Moustache Soldier tucked his hands under his protruding belly and licked his lips. "You are from Israel?" The goop on his whiskers trembled when he spoke. He scrutinized Maman's face. She had the Mediterranean olive-toned skin and dark hair that frequently made Israelis think she was one of them.

"Canada. United Nations." Maman pointed at the passports in his hands and flashed a toothy smile.

"Where is your husband?"

A third officer appeared with tiny cups on a tray. The bridge of his nose was crooked and lumpy, like he'd been in his share of fist fights. He and the senior officer exchanged glances.

I felt guilty, as if we'd done something wrong. But Maman didn't flinch. "My husband is here, on the Golan. With the UN."

"You will have coffee."

I was thirsty, but the cups were smudged with dirty fingerprints.

The soldier with the nose like a professional boxer's handed one to my brother first, who downed it in a gulp. Next was my mother. Whether it was the guard who fumbled or Maman's hand that grew unsteady, a large black stain spread over the left leg of her fancy camel-coloured pants.

The hot liquid must have burned her skin, but Maman sat with one silk-lined leg crossed over the other, hands folded on her lap, sunglasses pushed onto her head.

Crooked Nose said nothing. He extended a cup to me.

I shook my head. "No, thank you."

He gave it to me anyway.

I balanced the tiny cup and saucer on my lap. The thick, smoky liquid had a greasy film on top. My stomach roiled. At home, I drank tea, never coffee.

When the guard bowed his head to speak into his walkie-talkie, Maman leaned toward me. *"Bois-le,"* she hissed through a frozen smile. *"Sinon on ne partira jamais d'ici."*

It tasted as bitter as aspirin.

When we were escorted back to our car, Brad and Sharon were waiting in their brown Mercedes.

"I should have known better than to travel with only one pair of pants," Maman ranted once we were waved through the border. "Now I'll be dirty and smelly for three days."

"What about Kissa?" I turned around in the back seat and made a thumbs up to Sharon. She answered with the same. "Phew! He made it."

Etienne pointed at two women in burqas walking on the side of the road. "Maybe you two should get some traditional clothes. So you can blend in."

My mother snorted. Since the incident on Yom Kippur, we'd had several heated discussions about this. But she refused to buy me long skirts to satisfy the neighbours. She still insisted that, as foreign women, she and I could wear whatever we pleased.

I searched the landscape for points of interest. Everything looked the same as it had in Israel. Same palm, date, and banana trees. Same olive groves. The only difference was the road signs written in elegant Arabic lines and squiggles rather than boxy Hebrew.

"What if we get lost?"

"Don't worry! We're on the Damascus road." Maman laughed as if she'd told a joke but I had no idea what she found so funny.

When we reached the city limits, Brad slipped ahead of us and led the way to our hotel. They were too tired to tour and needed to tend to Kissa. They promised to meet up with us the following day. Until then, we were on our own.

On the streets of downtown Damascus, my jeans, sneakers, and short-sleeved shirt were an oddity. There were whistles and catcalls and stares from drivers and men on the street. I didn't know what to do with myself. I looked at the ground, the buildings, the sky, the trees. Anywhere but at the men. At home in Canada, I was one of those girls who studied hard and got good grades. I wore glasses. But even Leah Sheck, with her flipped bangs, designer jeans, and muscular, figure-skater legs did not attract this amount of attention when she walked around the playground in Yellowknife at recess.

"*J'aime pas ça*," I complained to Maman.

"It's your hair," she said. "They've never seen anything like it. Most people *in the country where we are living*," she paused dramatically and made big eyes at me, "originally came from various parts of Europe and then moved *to that country*," more big eyes, "after World War Two. But Syria hasn't known that kind of immigration."

A quick glance around the crowded street confirmed it. All the citizens of Damascus looked like they might be related.

Maman brushed her hand against the stain on her pants. She'd tried scrubbing it off in the hotel bathroom, then held a wet compress to her thigh for the duration of our restaurant meal. But the stain remained dark and defiant.

We stood on the sidewalk and watched the traffic go by on Baghdad Street. "The gold souk is south of here, in the Old City," Maman said. "But first, I may have to get a new outfit."

Etienne groaned. "I'll wait for you at the MAC House."

Brad had told us there were comfy chairs there, and

American movies on VHS, and a steward who would serve us soft drinks and run them up on a tab.

"No." Maman didn't hesitate. "We need you with us. For protection."

When Etienne raised an eyebrow and made a gun shape with his thumb and pointer finger, she didn't laugh.

By the time we reached the Old City the sun was high and the pavement was hot. I was thirsty. In the shop windows, gold chains were as thickly coiled as sailors' rope. They dazzled and glittered in the sun. "Like Ali Baba's cave," Etienne said.

"Or a dragon's lair." I was deep into *The Lord of the Rings* and hoped there would be time to read later on at the hotel.

"I'd like to get us each a little something." Maman stood in front of the store like a child in a candy shop. Her jewelry box, containing treasures Daddy had brought back from his trips, was her prize possession.

Beggars missing hands, legs, or feet rolled by on small square boards with wheels.

My hands cupped the few Syrian pounds in my pocket, sticky with sweat. On the corner of a narrow alley, I spotted a cart piled high with oranges. Maman and Etienne wandered down the street ahead of me admiring the gems on display in each window. I thought I'd surprise them by buying us each an orange.

I was selecting the brightest, juiciest looking ones when I felt a tug on my cotton T-shirt. A young woman grabbed my elbow and said something in excited Arabic. I would have pulled away and ignored her except that she had managed to get hold of the end of my braid and was twisting it around her brown fingers. If I tried to break free, it would hurt.

"My sister, you'll be my sister," she said in English. Her grasp was insistent.

"*Maman, viens,*" I called out.

My mother turned, her eyes two brown question marks. When she walked back toward me her limp was more pronounced than usual.

"Ah, good, yes, come. Please, this way," the young woman said, seeing my mother. She put her arm halfway around my shoulders so that she could hold both braids.

Etienne flashed me a fiendish grin while the girl led us down the street and through a small doorway on the side of a jewellery shop. A fatter, older woman was waiting there. She lifted the black veil from her face and pulled a wrinkled snapshot of an Arab man from under her burqa. She spoke lovingly in Arabic to the man in the photo and motioned to the young woman to translate.

"You marry him. We be sisters."

"We give gold," the old woman said. "Two hundred camels." Her voice sounded confident of the sale.

My brother seemed to think it was funny that I was about to be sold for a herd of camels to a man who looked to be in his mid-thirties in a photograph that was already quite old.

We were wedged in the narrow door frame. Both women had started touching my face when my mother grabbed my hand and walked backwards into the sharp afternoon light.

"Such an important decision," she said. "I must discuss it with my husband."

"Come back tomorrow. Here. We make plans."

"Yes. *Shukraan. Merci.* Thank you so much."

My mother smiled. We turned slowly, and walked down the street. When we got to the orange cart, we ran.

It was easy to outrun Maman. I slowed my pace to keep her at my side, even though I wanted to get as far away from the souk as possible. I wished I had something to throw over my bare head.

Once we were through the Old City gates, we stopped in front of a shop displaying burqas and traditional Arabian dresses with intricate beading. I pointed at a variety of head-wraps, displayed on styrofoam busts like Daddy used to shape his blue beret. "Please, Maman."

She bought us each a long silk scarf. I wound mine around my head and tucked my braids inside; she threw hers over her shoulder. "It will hang low enough to cover my stain," she said, putting her hand over her thigh.

Etienne picked out a black-and-white *keffiyeh* and had the sales clerk arrange it for him while he admired his reflection in the mirror. My mother said no, thank you, the scarf wasn't needed, but my brother refused to part with it.

"That's Palestinian garb," she hissed as soon as we'd exited the shop. "We can't bring it back with us."

Etienne jerked his chin at me. "It looks like our plans might change."

"Shut up." I scanned the street for the young woman, my mouth chalky with fear.

"Would you like to head home?" Maman asked the next morning over a breakfast of scrambled eggs at the hotel.

Etienne and I both nodded. I didn't want to go back out on the street. The sharp, tangy smell of the freshly squeezed orange juice on the table was nauseating. Etienne had just finished complaining that everything on the TV in our room was in Arabic.

"Don't tell Grandmaman about our trip." My mother's face looked as splotchy and tired as mine. She and I had both been awake most of the night, reading in the bathroom while Etienne slept. "Best that we wait to tell her once we're back in Montreal. She's already pretty frantic about us."

When she'd heard about the UN officers killed in Beirut, my grandmother had called us in the middle of the CBC newscast. When it was my turn to talk to her, she was still shouting into the phone as if she didn't dare turn the TV off in case there was more terrible news.

"It'll make for a great story. Once we're home."

"I could have been rich." Etienne took a sip of his hot chocolate. "I could have lived in a hotel like this year round." The whipped cream on his top lip quivered when he spoke. "Campfire story. How many camels do you think my sister is worth?" He'd been teasing me non-stop since the incident happened. "How much gold?"

When I kicked him, my foot caught the tablecloth. "Be careful!" Maman managed to steady the cups just as they threatened to spill. "We don't want to attract any more attention."

The steward at the MAC House connected us with a couple of Swedish officers headed to the Golan so that we could form a United Nations convoy. We gave hasty hugs to Sharon and Brad, with a promise to see them in Beirut in early January. After a relatively short interrogation at the border, we were back in our apartment in Israel by mid-afternoon.

When Daddy came home for supper, Maman and I were in the steamy kitchen, boiling noodles, making sauce, and baking brownies out of a mix we'd brought from Canada.

He stood in the kitchen doorway, taking in the messy scene. "You came home early." He wiped his glasses with his pocket handkerchief.

Maman reached over to kiss him. "I stopped at the Mahanayim Kibbutz and bought some herbs and hot chili peppers. I thought I'd make my spaghetti sauce — *comme à la maison*."

"I could bring some on observation post this week."

Maman wiped her hands on her apron. "I'll make you a tuna casserole with broccoli and penne pasta. And a tomato bisque. I want to use up the basil while it's fresh."

My father inhaled the rich kitchen scents. Maman's cooking was her art form. She knew which combination of spices would bring out the flavours of a dish.

"With food like this, I'll be the envy of all the other officers." He looked proud and satisfied — the monarch of a small, well-ordered kingdom.

My mother busied herself at the cutting board.

"How was Damascus?"

The French vowels were no longer soft or dreamy. I looked down into the pot of meat and tomato sauce I was stirring. Earlier that day, I'd written ten pages about the trip in my journal, supplying every detail, even though I doubted I could ever forget. But I didn't know where to start telling my father. I couldn't risk his laughter or criticism.

"I took the kids to the gold souk."

"Bring back any souvenirs?"

The silk scarf kept slipping off my head, I'd written in my journal. *I stuffed it into Maman's suitcase as soon as we got to the hotel. I never want to see it again.*

Maman added a dried herb to the pot I was stirring. Her face was wet with steam. Would she tell him about our near escape? Or would that be the same as admitting defeat? She studied the meat sauce as if she were reading tea leaves.

"I'm glad you got the tourism bug out of your system," Daddy said. He brought a piece of basil up to his mouth. "When's dinner? I'm famished."

Christmas Eve at our apartment in Tiberias, December 1982.

CHRISTMAS

Calvin: This whole Santa Claus thing just doesn't make sense. Why all the secrecy? Why all the mystery? If the guy exists, why doesn't he ever show himself and prove it? And if he doesn't exist, what's the meaning of all this? Hobbes: I dunno. Isn't this a religious holiday? Calvin: Yeah, but actually, I've got the same questions about God.

BILL WATTERSON, *CALVIN AND HOBBES*

When I came home from Efrat's one afternoon in December, Maman called me into her room. It was warmer in there than the rest of the apartment because of the space heater she'd set up. But when I saw the half-packed suitcase open on her bed and Etienne sitting next to it, my hands went clammy.

"Where are you going?" We weren't moving out of the apartment for another ten days. It was too soon to pack up all our clothes.

Maman had her head in the closet. "Daddy and I are off to Beirut for the weekend. To hunt for an apartment."

"What about me and Etienne?" My stomach roped itself into a knot. "Who will we stay with?" I was used to Daddy being gone for a week or more, but Maman was always home.

She had yet to look at me. I craved a comforting word. Some kind of reassurance.

She slipped one of Daddy's shirts off its hanger and spread it on the bed. "The Herreras were my first choice, but they're leaving for Bethlehem tomorrow." She folded the shirt into a small package. "So you'll both stay with Johan's family."

At the mention of his best friend, Etienne looked up from the *MAD* magazine he'd been flipping through. "But is Beirut safe? Everyone keeps asking me that." He threw the magazine onto the bed and made pretend machine-gun fire with his arm, causing the tiny green-and-orange kingfisher that had landed on Maman's bedroom balcony to fly off in a panic.

Maman pushed the magazine aside to make room for a sweater. *Escape the Insanity of the World! Go... MAD*, the cover instructed. "We'll choose an apartment on the Muslim side." She placed the folded shirt in the suitcase. "Away from the fighting."

My stomach knot tightened. I sat on the edge of the bed as if that could anchor me into place. Lara's father's death had made it clear that Beirut was no place for families. "I heard you say apartments over there are hard to find."

"Destroyed in the war?" Etienne didn't seem worried at all.

"Daddy's colleague has scouted out a few possibilities for us."

I didn't want to cry in front of my brother. I couldn't trust him not to call me a baby in front of Johan. "How long will you be gone?" The words came out garbled, as if I had coins under my tongue.

While she considered the shoes on the floor of her closet, Maman rubbed the spot between her eyes with two fingers as if she were scrubbing a stain off a shirt. "Just one night. We'll leave early tomorrow and return on the twenty-fourth."

"But that's Christmas." Now she had Etienne's attention. We all knew he was hoping for new skateboard wheels and his own boombox. "Why cut it so close?"

Maman tucked her walking shoes into the sides of the suitcase, then retrieved her headache medication from her purse. "It's the only time Daddy could get off. And we need someone to take us there, show us around, and help us. It's complicated."

Christmas was my favourite day of the year. We always went to midnight Mass and opened our presents when we got home. It was the only time our parents allowed us to stay up half the night. On Christmas morning, we played board games together. Even my father joined in.

This year, for the first time, I didn't care so much about the presents. I'd asked for clothes, since nothing I'd brought from Canada seemed to fit anymore.

I was a little excited about staying at Johan's house, just to be close to him. My journal was full of daydreams about my crush. But I hated the thought of Maman being gone.

After Etienne left, I watched her lay outfits on her bed. I offered to iron her wrinkly blouse, but she shook her head.

"You've got your own packing to do."

In my room, I took my schoolbooks out of my backpack, but I couldn't stop shivering. Compared to Maman's snug bedroom, the rest of the apartment felt damp and uncomfortable. Without central heating, it was colder than our house in Yellowknife had ever been, even in the heart of winter.

I went into the kitchen and turned on the oven. At the table, with my back to the open oven door, I folded white paper into squares and cut out intricate snowflake patterns. My fingers were numb with cold, but after a couple of hours I had a pile of tiny white cuttings, like snowflakes themselves, on my lap, at my feet, and all over the table.

When Efrat joined me after supper, we decorated our apartment walls and windows and trimmed the artificial, box-shaped Christmas tree with popcorn garlands and homemade gingerbread men. Once it was done, we called Maman to admire our work.

"These decorations will help Santa find us," she joked. We still played the Santa game, even though it had been a long time since I'd figured it out. But this year, I had bigger preoccupations. I wanted my parents to come back in time.

At the Nilssons', I was the only girl besides Johan and Kristoffer's mother, a lean woman with muscular curves, whose body and short, no-nonsense haircut made her look like an Olympic medalist. The three boys bunked together so that I could have my own room. I holed up like a soldier in a trench, making my way through the last of the teen paperbacks I'd brought from Canada, and only came out for meals.

I hoped the Beirut apartment would turn out to be a joke — like the summer house in Jericho Daddy had told us about last year on one of the darkest days of midwinter, when the temperature in Yellowknife lingered at negative forty degrees Celsius, and the fog blocked out our few hours of sun.

Six months after he told us about the Jericho house, as we drove from Jerusalem to Tiberias and deep in the desert, Daddy stopped the car on the side of the road and waved at a row of mud huts. "There it is! The one in the middle."

A small face with two coffee-brown eyes stared at us from one of the hut windows. "Looks like someone already lives there," I said, trying to mask my confusion with laughter.

My mother shifted in the passenger seat so I could see her face. "You didn't really believe him, did you?"

At the time, I'd felt silly, and everyone had teased me, saying I was easy to fool. But now I wished I could go back to being that girl in the car. Or better yet, the girl in Yellowknife, for whom this was nothing but a fantasy, like a mirage on the hot pavement in summer.

I hoped Daddy would change his mind and he and Maman would come back with pictures of a house by the sea in nearby Nahariya.

"It's movie night at the MAC House," Mrs. Nilsson announced over our supper of pickled herring and black bread. "We'll all go."

There would be popcorn. A story to make me forget my parents' trek into a war zone.

At the MAC House, I looked sideways down the row of chairs. Johan was sitting two seats from me, his long, tanned legs sticking out in front of him. He waved and winked, and I waved back. I was still hoping he would give me my first kiss before we left Tiberias, even though he consistently chose Etienne's company over mine.

I felt grown up watching a PG film without my parents. The week before, we'd been privy to a full screen shot of Richard Gere's bum in *An Officer and a Gentleman*. I hoped tonight's film would be a love story or at least a romantic comedy.

But *Tattoo* was neither. It featured a young man kidnapped by a cruel band of thugs who systematically tattooed his body. Each day he received a new mark, until his entire skin, even his face, was covered with ink. He was locked in a bare room, isolated from his family and all that was familiar to him. Over time, he became a stranger even to himself — unrecognizable, except for the eyes and hair.

I slunk down into my chair and kept my eyes closed for most of the second half.

"Gangsters in the Russian mafia get themselves tattooed all over," Etienne said on the way back to the Nilssons'.

"I've seen pictures in the Stockholm newspaper," Johan's father said from the front seat. "The tattoos identify which gang each man belongs to. They get them everywhere — even on the face."

"Cool," Johan said.

But the idea that someone could steal my name, my ideas, my memory, my privacy, and even my skin terrified me. Could I become unrecognizable even to myself? Could I be trapped inside my own skin?

In Yellowknife, I'd had nightmares about *The Boy in the Plastic Bubble*, a TV movie about a boy with a compromised immune system, forced to live in incubator-like conditions as contact with unfiltered air might kill him. The idea of being trapped without any means of escape made me wake up screaming.

Tattoo brought that nightmare into another dimension. That night at the Nilssons', I woke up several times in a sweat, covers thrown off, my hands clutched around my braids. Once I got over my confusion and remembered why I was in a strange bed, the first thing I checked was my skin. Had someone tattooed me in my sleep?

Then I remembered where my parents were, and thought of all the potential dangers that threatened them: Bombing. Disappearance. Kidnapping. Murder.

"You don't look so good," Etienne said over our breakfast of muesli and yogurt.

When I told him about my nightmare, he rolled his eyes and shovelled a spoonful of cereal into his mouth. "You're such a baby." Bits of granola sprayed onto the table when he spoke. But when I mentioned my fears about Maman and Daddy and that we might not see them again, his Adam's apple started to bob. He got quiet for a bit, pushing his cereal around in his bowl instead of eating it.

Mrs. Nilsson looked up from the exercise mat she'd spread out on the living room floor. "If your parents don't return in time, you can join us for Christmas dinner." She lunged forward onto her right leg, her left one stretched out behind her, calf muscle bulging.

"I'm going for a run. You'll be the lady of the house while I'm gone." She smiled, but her kindness made me miss Maman more.

Alone in my room, I knelt by my bed. "Come back," I prayed, calling on my mother the way I'd heard Grandmaman implore *la Vierge Marie*. "Find what you're looking for and hurry back to us. Please. Don't. Leave. Me."

But Maman and Daddy did not return at noon as planned. I sat on the couch near the window, where I could watch the road and see the kitchen clock. Each hour of the afternoon dragged on.

Etienne, Johan, and Kristoffer invited me to play Risk, but I got cornered in Australia and managed to get eliminated within the first hour of play, much to Etienne's delight.

Mrs. Nilsson asked me to help her make *Kanelbullar*, the traditional cinnamon buns, for Christmas morning. I chopped oranges and figs with one eye on the window, setting my knife down to peer outside at the sound of a car engine.

At five o'clock, she set the table for six and lit the special

Christmas candles. But I put the extra cutlery back in the kitchen drawer, then retrieved the kitchen stools from the dining room table and returned them to the counter. "My parents will be back."

Mrs. Nilsson had changed into a red dress and was arranging her pearl necklace in the hall mirror when a knock came on the door.

"Maman!" I buried my face in her neck. I didn't care if Johan saw me. I breathed in her scent: a mix of musky perfume and sweat. "What took you so long?"

"The border closed at five o'clock, and we made it through at 4:45!"

She reminded me of Sharon Windsor — twitchy eyes, windswept hair, a face lined with secrets. Her navy peacoat hung crooked — the brass buttons in the wrong holes — giving her a lopsided look. Her black, knee-high leather boots were splashed with mud.

"Will I have my own room?" I asked, holding my breath.

"Yes. We managed to find a three-bedroom apartment on the Muslim side. It feels like a small miracle." She apologized to Johan's mother for her lateness and grabbed our overnight bags.

"It was really hard to find something," she said, once we were alone together. "So much of the city is destroyed or off limits. We did the best we could." On the short walk back, she said nothing more about the apartment. She wanted to know all about my time at the Nilssons', as if I'd been at a birthday party sleepover. When I told her about my nightmare, she quickened her pace. "Don't be silly. That will never happen to you."

I wanted her to pull me into a hug, to whisper into my ear that she and Daddy would protect me from strangers, from harm, from any threat. Instead, she looked up and down the street and darted across, gesturing for me to follow. *"Dépêche-toi!* I want to freshen up and have dinner before we leave for the church."

Even though Daddy was smoking, it felt cozy to have the four of us in the car. Together again, and on our way to midnight Mass at St. Peter's, on the shores of Lake Galilee.

Maman checked her lipstick in the mirror behind the sun visor. "Christmas in the Holy Land. *Quelle chance!"*

I felt lucky to have my parents sitting in front of me, in one piece.

On the beach, around the church door, and in the garden milled a thick crowd of cats. They wound around our pant-legs, purring and crying for food. Their animal sounds mixed with a tinny "O Holy Night" playing on a tape recorder inside the chapel.

The cats' glow-in-the-dark eyes watched the fishing boats laden with nets out on the lake.

"It's just like in the time of Christ." Maman tried to loop her arm into Daddy's, but he shrugged her off, never keen to show affection in public.

I searched the squirming cats for signs of Minou's orange stripes. There were a few tabbies, but they seemed too old. One had an ear that flapped when it walked, like it had been almost torn off in a fight. Another had only half a tail.

"Don't even think about picking one up." Maman lifted the hem of her dress and pointed at the ringworm lesions on her ankle. I still had them too.

"Anyway," Etienne scoffed, "there's no way Minou could walk all the way here from our house. He's probably dead by now. Squished by a car or killed by a bigger cat."

"*Parle moins fort,*" Daddy said.

A bunch of English-speaking soldiers had arrived in army vehicles and were stooping to let the cats lick their palms and crawl into their arms.

I whispered Minou's name and searched for her until Maman insisted we take our places inside. The tiny stone church was stifling, packed with Canadian and American soldiers in combat uniform. We were the only family. In spite of being squeezed in, shoulder to shoulder, no one talked.

The priest made the sign of the cross over the congregation. "Peace. Shalom. Salaam. Pax. My peace I give you, says the Lord."

He had an enormous white beard — Santa-like — with wide Elvis sideburns. He'd slicked his hair back with water to tame it, but a few white curls popped up around his ears.

Some soldiers sat with their shoulders slumped forward. One man held a wrinkled photo of a woman and a baby. Another remained kneeling after the rest of us had sat down.

"There are no atheists in foxholes," the priest said. In

his gold-and-white outfit — a sharp contrast to the green-uniformed men — he looked otherworldly, like a prince.

Maman squeezed my hand but had to let go to wipe her eyes. Then she crossed her arms over her chest as if to protect her heart.

I leaned forward to gauge Daddy's expression, but it was his usual church face, expressionless as a statue. Etienne was dozing in the heat.

When we filed into the aisle to receive Holy Communion, many of the men were crying. It was hard not to stare. All my life, I'd heard my father say soldiers don't cry whenever Etienne started to sniffle or tear up. But it seemed Daddy had been wrong.

The priest made the sign of the cross over us. The burning candle on the altar cast giant shadows of his robed arms on the stone walls. "May you become the brother of God." He nodded at each man in turn. "And learn to know the Christ of the burnt men. Merry Christmas."

Startled by his benediction, I thought of the *grand brûlé* who lived on my grandparents' street in Montreal, his face rendered unrecognizable when his tent caught on fire during a camping trip. His garbled skin was like a Hallowe'en mask. What did these soldiers have in common with him?

Etienne crossed his eyes at me. "Over at last," he said in a stage whisper.

My father held us back from turning into the aisle. "Let the soldiers go first," he said. "To honour them."

"Where have they been?" I asked. "Where are they going?" We were accustomed to seeing Israeli soldiers in combat uniform in Tiberias, but these soldiers were different. "They're not where they want to be," Maman said. "They miss their wives and children. And their parents. Everyone wants to be home for Christmas."

I thought of Grandmaman and Grandpapa in Montreal. Their warm kitchen would be full of the smell of roasting chicken, Grandmaman's glasses foggy with steam while she stirred the gravy and steamed the carrots. I felt a stab of jealousy that my Québecois cousins would get to be there with them while we were stranded in Israel.

The Santa priest was hugging some of the men, holding them in his arms as if they were his kids. In the humid church, his white head had become a riot of curls.

I whispered to Maman, "What did he mean by the Christ of the burnt men?"

"*Les pauvres*," she whispered. "*Sans famille à Noël.*"

When we finally spilled into the cool night air, the priest had also made his way out and was surrounded by the mewling cats. He had a burlap pouch slung across his chest and was feeding the cats out of his hand.

Like many of the soldiers, my father lit a cigarette. He'd been smoking almost nonstop since he and Maman had come back from Beirut. "Look," he said to me, "he's celebrating a second Mass."

"It seems right," Maman said, her eyes on the priest as if she wanted to talk to him, "that nothing — not even a stray cat — be turned away tonight."

In the dark, she could have been mistaken for a child — the shortest person in the courtyard, hugging her arms around her delicate frame. *"Père,"* she blurted, "would you bless our family? We're moving to Lebanon in a few days."

The priest knelt to give food to a harlequin cat with black-tipped ears. *"Envoyez-ça en haut."* He pointed above his head. "Look for the Bethlehem star."

The sky was a tangle of constellations. I could pick out only the Big and Little Dippers and Polaris, the North Star, but I traced lines with my eyes and made up my own grouping, of a house with a fence and a flower garden near the sea.

Next morning, a knock at the door interrupted our breakfast feast of strawberry crêpes and whipped cream with Québec maple syrup. My first thought was of the Monopoly game I'd set up in the living room. My father had agreed to join us after our meal. I didn't want anything to prevent us from playing.

A man stood at the door in a black-and-white checkered *keffiyeh* with a knife stuffed into the belt of his pants. He let out a long sentence in Arabic, ending with the word "Beirut."

A lump the size of an Israeli grapefruit formed at the back of my throat. Maman grabbed my arm with one hand and Daddy's with the other.

While we watched, stunned, the man whipped out the knife with a war whoop.

This was it. Word had got out that we were leaving Israel for its enemy territory. We were done for.

But then, instead of thrusting the blade into my father's

chest, the man burst into laughter and pulled the covering off his head.

"A Christmas present." He handed the knife to Etienne with a grin. "And something to protect you from those crazy Arabs."

"Victor!" My father clapped his old friend on the back. "Would the Prince of Tiberias like some Baileys in his coffee? Or are you up for some Scotch?"

"I'll have it all," the man said. "Whatever you've got." He kissed my mother on both cheeks. But when he came toward me to do the same, I turned my face away and extended my hand for a shake. Instead of relaxing, now that I knew the man was a hoax, my body trembled even more. I couldn't control it.

"Anything I need, Victor finds it for me," Daddy said. "He keeps us supplied on the Golan." More grins and claps on the back.

"You found me the knife I wanted." Etienne polished the blade with his paper napkin while Victor removed its casing from his belt.

"I came here from Europe in '46. As a Zionist." He inspected the label on the whisky bottle and poured a slug into his cup. "I fought to make Israel what it is today. Anything you need, I know where to find it."

"Victor was a spy," Daddy said. "That's why he speaks Arabic. He fought in the Israeli war for independence."

"Nechama, my wife, and all my children were born here." Victor raised his coffee mug. "To Israel," he said, and clinked his cup with my parents'. "*L'chaim!* We will meet again in Jerusalem when you've finished your mercy mission, or whatever you call it." He took a loud slurp of his drink.

I wondered how long this guest was planning to stay.

"You're like the Holy Family, fleeing Israel," Victor said, to a fresh round of laughter around the table.

Maman was pouring maple syrup on Victor's pancakes when a second knock sounded at the door. At first, I was afraid to answer. My knees felt huge and wobbly, like a newborn colt's. But when I finally pulled the door open, Johan stood on the other side. His white-blond hair was swept back from his forehead like Tintin's.

"*God Yul*. Happy Christmas." He handed me a piece of paper. "I made you a present."

Not for Etienne. For me.

Johan's six-foot body filled the doorway. When he lifted his arm to drape it over the frame, I could smell the pine-cone odour of his deodorant. His face was close enough to kiss.

"Are you going to look at it?"

I remembered the piece of paper in my hand.

It was a picture of the three of us — Etienne, Johan, and me — holding hands and running across a map of the world. We each wore shorts and a T-shirt with the flag of our respective countries drawn on the front. Our skin was entirely tattooed, even our faces. Disembodied arms reached out to grab us from the edges of the continents.

"Cool, isn't it?" When I didn't answer, Johan added, "You recognize yourself, right? I figured the braids were a dead giveaway."

I didn't know what to do. His drawing both fascinated and terrified me. "Thanks." I reached up to kiss him on the cheek. His skin was bristly, like Daddy's at the end of the day. It smelled like Juicy Fruit gum. My whole body went electric.

"*God Yul*," Johan said again. "Tell Etienne to come and get me when he's ready for a skate."

I shut the door behind him and placed the paper against it. I folded it to hide Etienne. Then I folded away all the ghoulish figures until only a small square remained, showing Johan and me holding hands while our sneakered feet hovered over the edge of Israel, above the Mediterranean Sea.

Outside Damascus, Syria, December 1982.

FROM DAMASCUS TO BEIRUT

*I'm sure that someday children in school will study
the history of the men who made war as you study
an absurdity. They'll be astonished, they'll be shocked,
just as today we're shocked by cannibalism.*

GOLDA MEIR

Snow fell on Damascus.

"Your father took me here on my first visit to the Middle East, in '77," my mother said. "It was the day after a public hanging. The bodies were still dangling from the scaffolding." She wrapped her wool shawl more tightly around her shoulders.

I looked up. There was only a Syrian flag flapping in the December wind. A pair of grim-faced soldiers stood at attention next to the flagpole, machine guns with fixed bayonets slung across their chests. It was New Year's Eve, and we were walking through Sabaa Bahrat Square — Arabic for Seven Fountains — on our way to a fancy French restaurant to celebrate the end of 1982.

"They're talking about bringing capital punishment back in Canada," my brother said. "I read about it in *Maclean's*."

"Here in Syria, if you're caught stealing, they cut off your hand." My father made a slicing motion over his wrist. "Seems fitting."

"Depends on what you stole," Etienne said.

The damp penetrated my jean jacket and made me shiver. "What do you think those men did that deserved a hanging?"

Maman turned to look at me. "Do you really want to know?"

"They were probably spies, right?" Etienne asked. "Enemies of Russia?"

It made me nervous to think that the two superpowers — Russia and the United States — were each funding a different side of the war: Russia supplying arms and money to Syria, and the U.S. doing the same for Israel. What if the war in the Middle East escalated into nuclear conflict?

"They were murderers," my father said. "They killed an entire family."

"How?" Etienne asked.

"By pouring sand down their throats," my mother answered.

"Whoa," Etienne said. "That's crazy."

I tried to push the picture out of my mind, but it stuck there, freeze-framed, a scene in a horror movie. But worse, because it was true.

My father quickened his pace. "Let's forget about the war for tonight."

"Yes." Maman's breath came quickly. I wasn't the only one having trouble keeping up with my father. "We've booked a table at the best restaurant in the city."

"Do we have to stay there until midnight?" Etienne asked. "Can't we just bring some food back to the hotel instead?"

"No," my mother and father said at the same time.

"Tonight we celebrate," Daddy said. "Tomorrow we drive to Beirut."

I hugged myself. "I didn't know it could snow here."

"It doesn't, usually. The weather is abnormally cold," Daddy said.

"Is there anything normal around here?" Etienne mumbled.

We passed by a family of beggars huddled near the entrance of a mosque. A milky-eyed woman held her palm out toward us. A small child clung to her dress, while another played with a pile of small stones in the street.

I wished I had money to give them, but we'd left all our Israeli shekels in Tiberias with Daddy's friend Victor that morning. Since we were just passing through, Daddy hadn't given us any Syrian money.

It was the fanciest supper I'd ever eaten. Course after course of dainty vegetables and fine sauces served with fish, poultry, beef, and lamb. Pastries and chocolates and fine cheeses drenched in wine.

"Children, you must keep the menu," Maman said, collecting the ivory cards from the table and stuffing them into her oversized handbag. "We may never eat such a feast again." At midnight, the waiters in their tuxedos served us champagne. We were clinking our long-stemmed glasses together with cheers of *Salut! Bonne Année! Santé!* when the first gunshot sounded. The silverware rattled against the fine bone china. By the second shot, all conversation in the packed restaurant had ceased.

"Should we get under the table?" Maman clutched her handbag to her chest. It contained our passports — our most valuable possession — and ten thousand U.S. dollars.

Everyone in the restaurant was immobile and silent, as if we were all playing a game of statues. A third shot fired. A fourth. My stomach curdled. I fixed my eyes on my mother. She watched my father.

And then it was quiet. A minute or so passed. Someone shifted in his seat. A linen napkin fluttered to the floor, and a hand reached to pick it up. A low murmur of conversation began, like an insect buzz, until it grew and became a roar.

The waiters resumed their ministrations.

"Likely just a celebratory round of gunfire," my father said, raising his glass. "Here's to 1983 and our new life in Beirut."

"A new adventure," my mother said and clinked her glass against his. "Here's to keeping the peace in the Middle East." She smiled, but the quiver under her left eye betrayed her fear.

Etienne stifled a yawn.

"I suppose we should think about going," my father said. "Though I was hoping to have *un digestif.*"

Maman raised her eyebrows and puffed out her cheeks. We'd all had more than enough to eat and drink. But when the waiter came by, my father ordered a cognac for himself and an Irish cream for Maman.

"*Chérie,*" Maman said, putting her hand on his arm, "it will be an early morning."

But Daddy didn't budge. "A drink will calm your nerves."

My father took a wrong turn out of the restaurant, then walked off the sidewalk into the street.

Etienne snickered. "He's tipsy."

I pointed to Maman. She was hanging onto his arm but also walking a bit crooked. "So is she." I pretended to laugh. But ever since I'd heard the gunshots in the restaurant, I hadn't been able to shake my fear. I felt exposed, an easy target.

"Why can't we take a taxi back to the hotel?" I asked through chattering teeth.

"The exercise is good for us," my father said. "It will help us sleep."

Maman adjusted the silk scarf around her neck. "You can have a hot bath before going to bed."

But when we got back to the hotel, the power was out. The concierge unlocked our door and handed my parents a couple of candles. "Too much demand on the electric tonight," he said. "*Sana sa'eedah.* Happy New Year," he added over his shoulder.

"Imagine arriving in our new home on the first of the year," my mother said at six o'clock the next morning, while we waited for the American captain who would lead the way to Beirut in his UN jeep. "It's so symbolic."

"How long will it take to get there?" I asked. We'd been in the car most of the previous day, and I was tired of sitting.

"Normally, it only takes a couple of hours," my mother said.

"But the highway is often a battleground," my father said. "If we can't go through the Bekaa, we'll have to drive through the mountains."

"How long?" Etienne asked.

My father looked at his watch. "It depends on the roads. And the weather. Could be six hours. Or eight. Or ten."

My mother pointed at the approaching white jeep with the large black letters and blue UN flag. "Time to go."

Snowflakes landed on the hood of the car and disappeared. My shoes were still wet from last night's walk. I wished there was a wool blanket or something to wrap myself up in. With four of us in the small car, the windshield was steaming up. Daddy wanted the windows open to let in some air, but all we had was an ugly green army-issue poncho to keep us dry.

I had no idea what to expect on the other side of the border. I knew there was war, but what would that look like? What would it mean for us?

After half an hour of driving, we were deep into the mountains. The snow was thicker than in the city. A few inches accumulated on the ground, blanketing the mountainside in white. Cars slid across the road, and angry drivers leaned on their horns.

It wasn't long before traffic came to a standstill.

"Is there a bridge up ahead? Or is it a checkpoint?" My brother craned his head out the window.

Many of the drivers had left their vehicles and were leaning against them, smoking or talking in small huddles. Several men stared at me. Some whistled and called out. I felt gratified by the attention but unnerved as well. I tried to ignore them.

The thin, pale driver of the UN jeep came to talk with my father. "What do you think we should do?" he said.

"Turn around," my father said. "Head back to Damascus."

"Right." The man returned to his vehicle.

"How will we get to Beirut?" my mother asked.

"Tripoli," my father said. "It's the only way."

"But it's always a hotspot." Maman's voice trembled a bit. "And we have the children ..."

"*On n'a pas le choix*," Daddy said. There was no other option.

Soon we were snaking back down the mountain, toward the city. When the car fishtailed, my mother screamed.

"In Canada ..." Etienne said.

"We would have snow tires," my father finished for him.

"Why don't we just fly to Beirut?" I asked.

"We'll need this car for the next seven months," Daddy said. "Don't worry. I'll get us there."

Six hours on the other side of Damascus, the snow was so thick we could barely see the road.

"We need to stop for food," my mother said. *"Les enfants ont faim."*

"I don't want to lose the UN jeep. It's already so far ahead of us."

At my mother's insistence, we pulled over next to a white cement house with a Coca-Cola sign in the window. Next to it was a billboard with the face of Yasser Arafat in a black-and-white checkered *keffiyeh*. We were in PLO — Palestine Liberation Organization — territory.

"I'll see what I can find." My father motioned for Etienne to come with him.

"Toilet?" my mother asked the woman who stood in the shop doorway. The woman stared at her and said nothing. I thought maybe she didn't understand English. While we waited, I shifted from one foot to the other, a universal signal. Finally, the woman stepped aside and gestured behind a counter with various dried goods. The air was saturated with the spiced, oily smell of fried food. The woman pulled a floor-length curtain back, and I followed my mother into the stinky space. Out of the corner of my eye I could see my father buying a pack of Marlboros.

The toilet was a hole in the ground with a groove on either side. "You straddle the hole," Maman said, "like this."

I turned away and faced the wall, trying to discern patterns or figures in the black mould that crept down from the ceiling.

When we got back to the car, my father was smoking. "I bought you some food."

My mother sighed and lifted a soiled brown paper bag off her seat before getting in. The snow had turned to rain, and we had no choice but to eat in the car. Maman passed me a boiled egg on a limp tissue. "Eggs and chips," she said brightly. But the egg was boiled too soft, and the potatoes were cold and soggy with grease.

"After last night's feast, I thought I'd never be hungry again," she said. I remembered all the food we'd sent back to the restaurant kitchen, uneaten. All the extra bread on the breakfast table that morning. Why hadn't we taken it with us?

I couldn't help myself. I had to ask. "How close are we? How much longer?"

"We're about an hour from the border," my father said.

I comforted myself by thinking about the money in my mother's purse. Surely, wherever we wound up, it could buy us what we'd need to survive.

"A woman is less likely to get mugged," my father had said when he'd handed my mother the money. "They'll frisk me long before they'll dare to touch you." Maman had nodded and stuffed the thick wad of bills into the zippered pocket of her crocodile purse. "It's a man's world over here," my father had said. "No man would ever dream of giving his wife such a sum."

He'd laughed, but we knew he had money in his pockets — for bribes. We'd seen how a well-placed twenty-dollar bill could open an otherwise closed door or mollify an angry threat. My father knew all about *baksheesh*.

My father stopped the car at a PLO checkpoint near Tripoli, eighty-five kilometres north of Beirut. We could see the city ahead of us, built into the hillside. A guard in combat fatigues pointed his machine gun at the sandbags and pylons blocking the road. The spike-shaped bayonet fastened to the gun's muzzle gleamed in the light of the setting sun.

Armed soldiers had been on every street corner in Tiberius, and often rode the bus in full combat gear. It was a familiar sight, but not something I'd gotten used to. There was no Canadian equivalent — no neat conversion, like shekels to dollars.

My father rolled down his window and flashed his I.D. card, then gestured toward us. My mother pulled our diplomatic passports out of her purse, but the guard shook his head. "No go." He tapped the hood of the car with his bayonet, then made a u-turn motion with his free hand. "Tripoli." He waved a finger back and forth. "War."

As if on cue, the city skyline lit up. A deafening boom sounded. I felt it everywhere in my body, even my teeth.

"They've taken the city," my father said grimly.

Maman let out a stifled mewl. "Where do we go now? We'll never make it back to Damascus. It's getting dark. *C'est trop dangereux.*"

I sank lower in my seat. We couldn't go forward and we couldn't go back. We were stuck.

My father turned both his palms up and looked at the guard. "*Qu'est-ce qu'on fait?*" In Damascus, we'd discovered that Syrians sometimes understood French better than English.

I hated him for not knowing what to do. I hated the way Maman flipped through her ten-year-old tourist guide to Lebanon as if an answer to our problem would miraculously appear on its pages.

The darkening sky threatened a winter storm.

The guard gestured toward an olive grove to the left of the road. "Follow taxi."

"It's worth a shot," my father said to Maman. "No one knows their way around a city better than a taxi driver."

It seemed like a good plan. Except, I didn't see any taxis around. Ours was the only car on this stretch of road.

Another explosion, bigger this time, sent a flock of red doves hurtling into the sky in a panicked flap. Fear built a nest in every corner of my mind.

"You told me there would be a ceasefire for New Year's," Maman said over the birds' high-pitched whistles. Before Daddy could answer, she continued. "We should have known better. What were we thinking, coming here?"

"We had no choice," my father said. We'd tried to get to Beirut every other way.

Our legs were cramped. We'd run out of food. We hadn't seen the white UN jeep since noon.

"*Maudit Americain*," Maman said. "He was supposed to make a way for us. Keep us safe." She glared at my father as if he was to blame. "Your beloved United Nations has abandoned us."

I waited for my father to pull out a map. As a logistician trained to foresee any eventuality and plan for the worst, he was always prepared. But he headed into the olive orchard in the direction the guard had indicated. Frozen olives encased in ice and snow hung from the branches — treasures for the birds to find.

"This is kinda cool," Etienne said.

I gripped my armrest as the Peugeot bounced over the rutted ground.

"*C'est fou*," Maman said. This is crazy.

"It's our only hope," my father answered. "What do we have to lose?"

My mother held her head in her hands. "Where are we supposed to find a taxi?"

"I'm sure the guard will radio one," my father said. "He probably has a relative or friend nearby." He turned the hazard lights on.

After a few minutes, a beat-up Mercedes came up the road. Its windshield was cracked, its bent fender attached with duct tape. The driver's head was wrapped in a white and black checkered *keffiyeh* like Yasser Arafat.

My father hailed the driver with his free arm. "Taxi?'

The turbaned man made a thumbs-up and drove closer to us.

"Beirut," my father called out the open window. No response. He repeated more slowly, and with a French accent, "Beyrouth."

The driver's face was pockmarked, as if he'd had a bad case of measles as a child. He nodded, then rubbed his forefingers with his thumb.

This was going to cost us.

My father pulled a few bills out of his pocket.

The driver asked for more.

"You'll get the rest at the end of the drive," my father said. It was a relief to see him back in control.

The Mercedes left tracks through the olive orchard that we tried to follow. But the terrain was pot-holed and muddy — better suited to a horse-drawn cart than a car.

"Olive trees are astonishingly tough," my mother said in a wobbly voice. "The wood is rot-resistant, and if the top of the tree dies out, a new trunk can grow up from the roots."

"We don't care," Etienne said.

But the trees did hold a certain fascination. They were gnarled and bent, with thick, mangled trunks. I thought of the Garden of Gethsemane that we'd visited in Jerusalem — a peaceful, gated oasis on the edge of the bustling Old City. But on that trip my father had been our confident, knowledgeable tour guide, and we'd been tourists.

This was different. We were going to Beirut to live. We were supposed to be there for the next seven months. The city was at war with itself as well as with Israel. It was under siege. And yet it was our destination. The further the taxi led us, the more I wanted to turn around and head back the way we'd come.

The last few rays of sunlight illuminated the silver leaves that clung to the gnarled olive branches.

"I think I heard a warbler," Maman said. "They like to nest in olive trees."

"Those sounds come from the taxi," Etienne said. "It's about to fall apart."

"Wait till you see the cars in Beirut," my father answered. "Some of these Mercedes are ancient. They're like tanks."

The comparison sent a shiver through my chest and shoulders. We'd seen barbed-wire compounds full of tanks on both sides of the Israeli–Syrian border as we travelled through the Golan on our way from Tiberius to Damascus. I'd observed the tanks with interest, from the relative safety of the car. But that was as close as I wanted to get.

The car lurched to a stop. My father shifted gears and pressed on the gas. The engine revved but the car didn't budge. We were stuck in the mud.

I tried not to think of Lara's father. Maybe he'd been killed not far from here.

My father opened his door. "You'll all have to push."

Etienne, my father, and I leaned our weight against the back of the car while my mother sat behind the steering wheel and followed my father's instructions. In the trees around us, Maman's warblers took up their song.

I kept my feet in the ruts the taxi had formed.

Etienne jutted his chin at the taxi driver, who waited in his car a bit further down the row of trees. "Why doesn't he help us instead of sitting there and watching his meter run?'

"He is helping us," my father said. "He's not sure who we are. We could be spies. Or enemies. He's already taking a risk."

It was almost dark by the time we got moving again. The driver took us to a road that led to a mountain range in the distance. Once he'd collected his final payment, he waved goodbye. We were on our own.

What had started as a drizzle when we left the orchard had now become a light snow. My toes were frozen. My father turned the heat in the car up to maximum but it barely made a difference.

The more we climbed, the more the snow thickened. The stagnant air in the car made me drowsy. I leaned my head against the window and imagined myself back in Yellowknife at William McDonald Junior High, where my friends were probably spending New Year's Day roller skating around the gym, listening to Casey Kasem's Top Forty Year-End Countdown on the radio. I skated round and round with them as the tunes played in my head. I was halfway through Stevie Nick's *Edge of Seventeen*, skating backwards with Catherine, when my father's loud voice, almost a shout, jolted me awake.

I squinted into the darkened car. Snow pelted against the windshield. The car's brights made it look like we were stuck in a blizzard.

My father was leaning into the passenger side of the car, his cheeks almost touching my mother's shoulder.

Next to me, Etienne swore under his breath. "What the—?"

The windshield wiper on my father's side was gone.

"It must have snapped off because of the weight of the snow," my mother said. The tremble had crept back into her voice, like a vibration on a violin string.

"Damn European cars aren't made for winter weather." My father pulled over and leaned out the window to wipe the windshield with his sleeve.

He had to repeat this procedure every few minutes. The wet snow was falling at a furious rate.

With the window down, snow flew onto the back seat. I pulled my father's khaki, army-issue rain poncho over my head to keep dry and tucked my feet underneath me. The coat smelled like it had been rolled up in someone's mildewy basement.

The snow turned to sheets of icy rain. The was no moon to light our way; no other cars or dwellings in sight.

Machine gun fire split the night sky.

"Get down!" my father shouted.

I hurled myself to the bottom of the car, heart pummelling, the poncho over my face like a plastic mask, stealing my breath.

My mother pleaded with Daddy. *"Penche-toi. Je te supplie, penche-toi."* Get down. Get down. Get down.

More firing.

We were the target.

I couldn't see; I couldn't breathe. "Hold my hand," I begged my brother, reaching for him through the folds of the poncho. But he refused to take it.

The firing stopped. I wrestled out of my cramped position, ripped off the poncho, sucked air into my mouth.

A masked guard was banging on my father's window with his bayonet, shouting angry words in Arabic. Etienne and I stared at the gun pointed at our father.

Daddy pressed his identity card against the snow-streaked window. "United Nations," he repeated in a calm voice. He pointed to the missing windshield wiper, then lifted his hands, palm facing up, in a gesture of helplessness I had never seen him do before.

Finally, the masked guard pointed at the road with his weapon, and we drove forward into the night.

"I didn't see the checkpoint," Daddy said. "I'll be more careful. There will be more as we approach the city."

My mother was furious. For the next hour, she ranted about the American captain who'd abandoned us. "Did he forget that we have children in here?" her voice rose with each syllable until she was shouting into the car. "His negligence could have gotten us killed. Without the UN jeep, we're nothing. Just civilians. Unprotected."

"He must have gotten scared and decided he couldn't wait," my father said. "Don't demonize him."

But that just made her madder. "I hate him," Maman said. "I hate that man."

The broken windshield wiper forced us to a crawl. My father leaned out the window and wiped the windshield with his sleeve.

We arrived in Beirut around nine o'clock, after more than twelve hours of driving. Kerosene lamps and candles lit the shops and homes we passed.

"The city is in a blackout," my father said. "Typical."

"I have to go to the bathroom," I said.

He stopped the car in front of a small restaurant fragrant with the aroma of roasting chicken. "You'll have to go behind this building."

Hunger gnawed at me with sharp teeth. A skinny German shepherd sat at attention near the entrance, next to a mound of wet garbage. I'd always been scared of dogs, especially after living in the Arctic, where fierce huskies roamed near wild.

"I'll go with you," Maman said. "It may take us a while to find our apartment building. Never mind the dog." But I could tell by the way she eyed it that she was scared, too.

"What if someone sees me?"

"I'll hide you," Maman said. "Pretend we're camping."

Since we'd entered the country, everything in Lebanon felt off-kilter, as if I'd removed my glasses and was trying to make sense of things through myopic eyes.

"We'll take these to Ghyslain," my father said, when he came back to the car with two roasted chickens and some huge rounds of pita bread. "He's got our keys."

My mother held the chicken out in front of her. It was dripping onto her feet and making a mess. But the smell of it was like a miracle.

"Give me a piece to eat while we're waiting," Etienne said.

"No," Maman said. "We'll eat at the apartment, with Ghyslain. He's done a lot to help us already."

I was hoping for a fire in the fireplace. Hot tea. But when we pulled up in front of the apartment building — a seven-storey cement building with a huge rubber tree in front — Daddy's friend was waiting in his car.

"*Bonne Année!*" He greeted my mother with a kiss on both cheeks and then shook my father's hand. "*Bienvenue à Beyrouth*," he said, wielding a large key ring. His cheeks and nose were thread-veined, his eyes yellow like a coyote. Wires and antennas spilled out of his pockets, and he had a radio attached to his belt under his protruding belly. He spoke to my parents in rapid-fire French and seemed to know all about the fighting in Tripoli. I would soon learn that Ghyslain knew everything about everything; he was an intelligence officer. His job was to extract information from all his various sources about where the fighting was to take place in and around the city.

We stumbled up the stairs and into a dark, damp space.

"Luxury!" Ghyslain said. "Three bedrooms, three bathrooms, full kitchen. What a find." He flicked his cigarette lighter, and my father did the same.

"I brought candles." He pulled them out of his breast pocket the way a magician might pull a rabbit out of a hat and held his lighter to the wick. Next moment, he was smiling broadly and slapping my father on the back. "Time to celebrate!" he said. "*Votre cadeau du Nouvel An.*" And then to my brother, who was staring at him, "In my family, growing up, we gave presents on New Year's Day. Christmas was purely religious."

"Yes," my mother said. "Many French Canadian families did that." But I knew that hadn't been true of her family.

Already this man had said more to us than my father had said on the entire drive from Damascus. I liked the way his generous words pushed back the darkness and filled the emptiness around us.

"We almost didn't have Christmas this year," I blurted. "Maman and Daddy barely made it back in time."

"I know," he said. "Your mother was beside herself, thinking the border might close. She kept reminding us her children were in Israel, as if we didn't know that." He put his arm around Maman's shoulders. *"Une vraie mère poule,"* he said. A mother hen. His belly jiggled when he laughed.

"You're going to love Beirut," Ghyslain said. "My daughter Manon got engaged here last month. Drove up with me from Nahariya to buy her engagement ring on Hamra Street. Largest diamond I've ever seen. The thing was as big as my thumbnail."

I could hear my father walking through the apartment, opening doors, the smell of his freshly lit cigarette trailing behind him.

"Can we eat now?" Etienne sat at the dining room table with his coat on.

"This is the best chicken you've ever tasted," Ghyslain said. "I'm sure of it. They roast it over the fire all day, basting it with *baharat* — a spice blend. And the bread!" he added. "Best pita ever."

He made it sound as if we'd entered the Promised Land.

"I brought some wine," he called to my parents, who were whispering together in the darkness. "Did I tell you this place comes with a cleaning lady?"

"Really?" My mother stepped forward.

Ghyslain was making wax drip from the candle onto a dinner plate. He fixed the candle in place. "Hold this," he said to me, while he prepared to do the same on another plate.

"This city has so much to offer." He sounded like a TV commercial. "I brought army sleeping bags for you, so you won't need to bother unpacking your boxes until tomorrow."

My belly was full, and I had my own room. Tomorrow I'd have my stuff. Things were looking up.

My mother was pouring tea for everyone from a thermos that Ghyslain had brought when a loud sound banged against the walls and rattled the windows. The wide-cushioned caramel-and-red striped sofa slid forward and then sideways.

My mother missed the cup and spilled tea over the tabletop. "Don't bother about that." Ghyslain wiped the spill with the paper bag that had been used to wrap the chicken. It soaked up the tea but spread grease everywhere. "It's just shelling in the mountains."

My mother put her hand on Ghyslain's arm. "Stop," she said. "You're making it worse."

My father pulled the heavy drapes back from the sliding porch doors. In the distance, we could see lights, as if a giant fairground had suddenly lit up the horizon.

"It's so loud." Etienne pulled one of the sleeping bags out of its pouch and wrapped it around himself. It was the same colour as the army poncho we'd had in the car.

I grabbed my small backpack and a sleeping bag. "Do we have flashlights?" I asked. But a fresh explosion drowned out my words.

In the mountains between Syria and Lebanon, New Year's Day, 1983.

~

MISSING

~

The world, that understandable and lawful world,
was slipping away.

WILLIAM GOLDING
LORD OF THE FLIES

There were only a few dozen students left at the American Community School of Beirut, but almost every continent was represented. Annexed to the American University and the U.S. embassy, it charged exorbitant rates for an American education in Lebanon. "A privilege for us to send you there," Maman said, a few days after we'd arrived in the city. "*Très prestigieux*. All children of diplomats."

"You'll walk there and back," our father instructed us. "Stay together and stick to the path I've marked out for you."

The hour-long walk — a winding path through the streets of Beirut that my father judged least dangerous — terrified me. It took us by bombed-out buildings, junked cars, a legless man begging for food. "Talk to no one," my father said. "Keep your heads down. Walk quickly."

The high school was nothing like tiny Mildred Hall Elementary in Yellowknife, where I'd been one of the oldest kids. Our new school had students from twelve to eighteen, and I was among the youngest. Besides American history and geography, English, French, science, math, art, and music, each student had to participate in after-school sports. In January and February, all the girls between twelve and fifteen were expected to play basketball.

Coach Michaels did not have the luxury of choosing his players. Since the Israeli invasion, the escalation of the civil war, and the subsequent evacuation of most diplomats, there were only three or four girls in each grade.

Our first game was against a team of gigantic, muscular Lebanese girls in shiny green uniforms. When they spoke to each other in Arabic, I was convinced they were talking about me — how goofy I looked in my pink sweatpants and glasses.

They'd brought a contingent of mouthy fans dressed in their school colours. *"Les grosses Américaines,"* they called us from the bleachers, though by the puzzled looks on my teammates' faces, I guessed not everyone understood their French. *"Retournez chez vous,"* one tall girl said before elbowing me in the side.

The referee heard her and blew his whistle. *"Penalité pour paroles grossières.* Language," he translated for Mr. Michaels and the other teachers and players. Off she went to the bench, but not before hissing *chienne* at me under her breath. It was the first time I'd ever been called a bitch.

The game was rough. Twice someone wrenched the ball out of my hands. Sharp nails clawed my arm. I was knocked to the dusty gym floor, where the same tall girl stepped on my braid and yanked it hard. Intense pain seared my scalp, above my right ear. The whistle blew, but I barely had time to get up before the game resumed.

"I need a break," I told Coach Michaels.

"We don't have a replacement for you. Get back in there." He kept his eyes on the court.

I felt clumsy and self-conscious, an embarrassment and a burden to my team, there only to provide the requisite number of players.

During half-time, I tried to catch my breath on the bench while the other girls chatted and preened. I decided I hated basketball. Chasing a ball around the court and trying to steal it from the other players felt stupid. Just before the start of the second half, I slipped off to the girls' bathroom, then locked myself in a stall. I rested my schoolbag on the pipes behind the toilet and pulled out the cigarette I'd snuck from my father's pack earlier that morning. I put the lid down and sat cross-legged on the toilet seat. I couldn't hear the shouts from the gym, or the pounding of the ball on the parquet floor. Just my own laboured breathing. My cheeks still burned, and I knew if I looked in the mirror they'd be bright red, with a white circle around my mouth. My lungs ached from all the running, my scalp still stung, and my right calf was quivering.

How long would it take Coach Michaels to note my absence? Part of me wanted him to come after me, knock on the toilet stall, and talk to me through the door. But I knew he'd be more focused on the scoreboard. Why leave the team to chase after the least valuable player?

I held the cigarette between my index and middle finger the way I'd seen my father do countless times. I enjoyed the tangy smell of the tobacco and the way the cigarette made me feel grown up and sophisticated, like my fathers' sisters. But my mouth was dry. The cigarette paper stuck to my chapped lips. The match burned all the way up to my mouth, where I held it against the cigarette with a shaking hand. The end caught fire and began to smolder. Pungent grey smoke curled up around my head. Soon it would drift over the stall and into the bathroom. Perhaps it would even seep into the girls' locker room and eventually find its way to the gym, where it might settle on Mr. Michael's thin grey hair.

When I inhaled deeply like my Aunt Suzette, acrid smoke filled my mouth and lungs. I coughed, spluttered, and dropped the cigarette onto my running shoe, where it burned a small hole through one of the nylon laces. I couldn't even get this right.

But I didn't really want to smoke. I wanted to get caught smoking. I wanted my parents to be alerted and summoned to the school: *Come immediately. Your daughter is in trouble.*

School had always been my refuge. I'd try hard to please my teachers and perform well, then soak up every word of their praise. But this was different. I wanted my parents' eyes on me.

Enough. I would leave. Wander the school grounds. Try to get past the guards at the gate. But I was too scared to walk alone in the ravaged city. Almost every day there were car bombs. I couldn't do it without my brother. I'd have to wait until the game was over. I threw the cigarette into the toilet and stood in front of the large window. Beyond the campus wall were city streets, apartment buildings. Further off, a strip of sea. In the water were five American warships with their cannons aimed directly at me.

A buzzer sounded, signalling the last fifteen minutes of the game. I grabbed my backpack and pulled out the Swiss army knife my father had given me on a camping trip up north. Our family had gone fishing for pickerel on Great Slave Lake and had to clear our own site. He produced a knife for me, almost as big as my brother's, and set me to cutting back the brush to make room for our four-man tent. When we got home, my father sharpened the blades for me with a special file. Now, one year later, knife in hand, I watched a helicopter land on one of the ships. Maybe it was my new friend Ginnie's father, bringing food, magazines, and supplies to the American Marines on board.

I ran my finger over the smooth metal of the knife. It felt cool and heavy in my hand. I flicked open the smallest blade, then the middle one, and finally the biggest.

I laid the biggest blade flat against the inside of my wrist, and slid it along the blue vein that protruded. I poked the sharp end into my skin. I flinched, but nothing happened. Pushed harder. Still no blood. Sawed at the skin until I broke the surface. I wanted to feel pain. A sharp physical pain that would take over the numbness I felt inside.

I continued sawing until drops of blood formed. I wanted to cut deeply enough that it would form a scar. I thought about the tree stump on the edge of my parents' bookshelf. As a young man at his family's cottage in Témiskaming, my father had carved his initials and my mother's into an elm tree and encircled them with a heart. Years later, when the tree grew diseased and had to be cut down, my parents kept the stump as a memory of their courting days.

I wanted them to see this wound I was making and acknowledge my pain. I wanted it to hurt more than this.

A drop of blood fell onto my pink sweatpants. It soaked purple through the cotton, then turned brown as it dried. The numbness inside me had not gone away. If anything, it had increased.

Another buzzer sounded, followed by a cheer. I pressed toilet paper against my wrist while I changed out of my gym clothes. I had to get out of the locker room before the Lebanese girls came in, cocky over their victory.

I found Etienne in the crowded gym, waiting near the door. To get to him, I had to pass behind the coach, who was leaning into Mr. Turner and some other teachers, discussing the game. I wondered if they would call me aside and ask where I'd been, but they did not seem to register my presence.

"What took you so long?" Etienne walked a few paces ahead of me. Not a word about the game. No mention of my disappearance. My pathetic game of hide-and-seek had fallen flat. No one had even noticed I'd been gone.

When we got home, Maman was in a flap. "The power is off, and the oven stopped working," she said by way of hello. She wiped her hands on her apron. "How was your day?"

Etienne dropped his schoolbag in the hallway and went straight to his room, shutting the door behind him.

"*J'ai faim.*" I tugged the sleeves of my hoodie down over my wrists, then stuffed both hands into the kangaroo pocket at the front. I wanted Maman to hug me, ask about the game, maybe smell the cigarette smoke in my hair.

"It's Daddy's birthday, and my *gigot d'agneau* is sitting in a cold oven." She picked up the telephone receiver, listened, placed it back onto its cradle, and picked it up again. "Still no connection. How am I supposed to reach your father to ask him to pick up some rotisserie chicken on his way home?"

The rich, lingering aroma of roasting meat and fried onions made my stomach growl. I assessed the contents of the pantry cupboard: a jar of peanut butter, a couple cans of sardines, some soda crackers, a new box of cornflakes, and a bottle of hot sauce. I shut the cupboard door a little too hard, so that it slammed.

Maman picked up the phone again, then put it back down as if it were a fragile thing that might break if mishandled. It would often take us twenty-five attempts before making a connection. Even then, our conversations could be cut mid-sentence.

"By the time Daddy makes it here then heads back across the city for the chicken, it'll be bedtime." I paused. When Maman didn't answer, I added, "And what if he's late?"

"Why don't you set the table? He'll be here soon."

All my life, my mother had insisted on a sit-down meal every night at six, though since moving to Beirut, my father often came home late. She would spread a tablecloth and dim the lights. Serve a home-cooked main course with at least two different vegetables, followed by a cheese platter and dessert, and finally a pot of black tea, piping hot, the way my father liked it. Back in Canada, our friends often asked if they could stay for supper, even before we'd thought to invite them.

"Use the red embroidered tablecloth from Damascus," Maman said. "To make it look festive." I laid a fork, butter knife, and spoon at each place, folded a napkin under the side plates, then remembered the promised meat and added a sharp steak knife to each place setting, on the right of the dinner plate, directly below the overturned water glass. With each movement of my hand, my cotton sweater brushed against the fresh wound at my wrist and made me wince.

"I found cornflakes at Smitty's today," Maman said. "Cost me a small fortune, but I thought you'd be pleased. And have a look at the birthday cake I bought at the Belgian pastry shop." I knew it was cruel not to say anything, but the secret pain at my wrist made me want to punish her.

"Maybe we could take the car to get the chicken," I said, even though I knew what her answer would be. She hadn't gotten behind the steering wheel since we'd left Israel. On top of that, darkness meant danger. Kidnappings. Killings. We rarely went out at night, and never without my father.

"The roadblocks ..." She didn't look up from her novel,

though she hadn't yet turned a page. "It's impossible to drive without traffic lights or stop signs, or police officers or even proper sidewalks ... When you get older you'll understand ..."

I understand already, I wanted to say. *I understand that it would be better to live anywhere but here.*

When it grew too dark to read, I lit the candles on the dining room table. Maman had set a wrapped birthday present on Daddy's empty plate.

"Maybe we should have some bread while we're waiting," she said. "Can you get Etienne?"

She was still in the living room but had stretched out on the couch and covered herself with the green-and-yellow knitted afghan we'd brought from Canada.

I lit the two pillar candles on the coffee table, then walked over to my brother's room, striking matches along the way. The light cast eerie shadows on the corridor walls. I let the matches burn right down to my skin, then blew them out just as they singed me. A blister formed on the top of my middle finger. It would hurt to hold my pencil.

I knocked on my brother's door, listened, then knocked again. "Etienne!" No answer. I turned the knob and went in. He was lying on his bed in the dark, the curtains drawn. I lit another match. His eyes flicked over to me.

"Coming to eat?" When he still didn't answer, I walked over to his desk and lit the candle in the empty wine bottle. "Cornflakes for breakfast tomorrow," I said. "Peanut butter and bread tonight."

He closed his eyes and rolled over to face the wall.

"Etienne is working on a school project," I told my mother

when I got back into the living room. "He'll eat with you later." I wanted it to be true. I wanted everything to be normal.

"I wish your father would call. Imagine him working at a communications headquarters and not being able to get in touch with his wife to say he'll be home late." Maman laughed, but there was no mirth in her voice. "He could have sent word through Ghyslain or asked one of the other men to stop by."

After another hour of study, I was getting ready for bed when there was a knock at the door. I came out of my room wearing my kangaroo sweater over my pyjamas. Maman was standing in the hallway, near the door. She had the afghan around her shoulders like a cape and was holding her book against her chest.

"Who do you think it is?" she asked. The candlelight made her dilated pupils look huge, reminding me of the doll-like people on the cover of my *Precious Moments* diary.

"Etienne!" I called his name a few times, but he didn't respond.

The knock came again, harder this time. We never had visitors at night.

"United Nations business," said a muffled English voice on the other side of the door.

My mother undid the deadbolt and gave the heavy, bullet-proof door a strong tug. In the doorway stood a man in a blue beret and a khaki uniform with a Canadian flag next to the United Nations crest on his chest. "Mme Bellehumeur?" he said. "Captain Guy Wilson, Air Force." The small golden wings sewn into the fabric above the man's name tag made me think of a guardian angel protecting him from disaster.

He lifted his blue beret, exposing a bald pate. The beret had a fold in the side; when he tried to place the cap back on his head, it stood up straight, giving him a comical appearance. He was taller and thinner than my father, with a narrow waist and spidery legs. His shoulders were slumped forward, an unusual posture for a military man.

"I work with your husband." His eyes flitted nervously from my mother to me.

"*Oui*," Maman said. "*Je vous connais.*"

The man opened his mouth, then closed it again. Why was he introducing himself to us? We'd met him several times already since our arrival in Beirut.

When the man brought his hand up to his head to fiddle with his beret again, his fingers were shaking so violently that he couldn't get them to settle into a grip. His fingernails were red and raw, chewed down to the nubs, and the pinky had dried blood on it.

"The major — Don — has gone missing," he blurted. "Beirut has been declared a theatre of war."

My mother glared at him. "Tell me what happened." Her words came out tight and clipped. It was the voice she used to stop a fight between Etienne and me. She'd sit us down and get us each to tell our side of the story, one at a time, like a referee.

I moved a bit closer. When I put my arm around her, I could feel her bones pressing into the palms of my hands. Bird shoulders, I thought. She always looked small beside my father's six-foot frame. Now she was smaller than me, the shortest one in the family.

"The major's voice came over the radio this afternoon, saying his jeep was under fire at a checkpoint near the Green Line. He was giving his coordinates when we heard machine-gun volley and rocks flying. Then the radio went dead. We haven't heard from him or his partner since three this afternoon."

"He was with Officer Thibeau?" My mother was still using her referee voice, but I could hear her breath quickening. "*Le Belge?* Perhaps they went on one of their reconnaissance missions ..."

My father's usual patrol partner was the frequent subject of stories at the dinner table because of his passion for French pastries. According to my father, "*Le Belge*" was on a first-name basis with the owners of all the small bakeries and *pâtisseries* in Beirut, and made regular visits to them while on patrol in the various districts of the city, claiming that he was cultivating friendships with the locals. "If I keep hanging out with Thibeau, I'll soon be shaped like a tea cozy, just like him," my father had said at table recently, causing us all to laugh.

But the pilot was shaking his head. "They are missing in action. Believed to be dead."

The afghan slipped from Maman's shoulders. She pulled it tighter, dislodging my hand. I let my arm fall to the side. We stood in a silent triangle in the doorway. The words would not come in either language. My mother did not invite the man to sit down, even though he was shaking profusely now and had to lean against the door frame to steady himself.

Daddy is dead. He won't be coming home again. Ever.

The officer wiped his eyes with his green, army-issue pocket handkerchief. *"Je suis désolé,"* he said in miserable French.

"You may go now." My mother measured each word with forced calm. She'd talked like this on our first day in Tiberias when my brother had appeared at the door bloodied and scraped, claiming he'd run into a barbed-wire fence by accident while exploring the field next to our apartment building.

She turned her back to the man, dismissing him, then grabbed the telephone receiver. I could see the whites of her knuckles as she dialed the numbers. She ignored the sniffling pilot and stared at the blank wall above the telephone stand. Her shadow on the wall loomed large and menacing.

"Ghyslain," she said into the phone. For once, the telephone connection had worked on the first try. *"Donald est disparu."*

"Tell Vaillancourt we heard it on the Op.Net — the operations network," the pilot said. The wings on his uniform moved up and down with each heave of his chest.

My father is dead. Dead. Dead. Dead. I wanted to punch the stupid, scared man. I wanted to kick him, hard, until he backed out of the door, doubled up in pain, wincing and bleeding.

"Merci d'être venu," I said instead. "Thank you for coming."

As soon as I shut the door, my mother said, "I've always disliked that man." She put the telephone back in its cradle. "He's scared stiff. Anyone can see that. *Il a peur de son ombrage,* scared of his own shadow. He's a coward. Your father told me. So scared, no one wants to work with him. He should be sent back to Canada on the next plane."

I followed her into the kitchen, where she opened the door of the supply closet and pulled out the ammonia and bleach, the mop and bucket.

"Hold the candle closer so I can find the rags," she said, putting her head in between the shelves.

"You're cleaning?" I asked. "But it's nine o'clock ... there's no power ..."

Daddy is dead. Daddy is dead. He's not coming home again. He's dead. Dead. Dead.

"This place could do with a good clean." She was already at the sink, running water into the bucket. The bitter smell of ammonia filled the kitchen. My eyes started to itch and burn.

"Should I get Etienne?" I walked toward the hallway and bedrooms. Surely he should know. How would we tell him?

"Let him sleep." Maman swept the kitchen floor, even though it was too dark to see anything, let alone crumbs under the counter. "Take the mop and follow behind me. Don't be stingy with the water. When we're done in here, we'll do the bathrooms."

"Even that one?" I pointed my chin toward the door at the left of the kitchen entrance. On the day we'd moved into the apartment, my mother had declared that bathroom condemned and put a big X made of duct tape on its door. The toilet was so black she swore it had never been cleaned. There had been cockroaches travelling up the pipes.

"No. We're doing fine without it. I found some furniture polish in a shop on Hamra. We'll use that on the mahogany in the living room. Give it a good shine."

We cleaned for an hour, moving the candles along with

us, making slow but steady progress in the darkened kitchen. I stepped onto the balcony to empty the bucket water onto the floor, as I'd seen the Lebanese cleaning lady do more than once. The night sky was brilliant with stars. I leaned on my mop and searched for the North Star and the Big Dipper.

"Remember when you were little, on the Valcartier base, and Daddy went away to the Middle East for six months?" Maman had come up behind me. Her voice was soft and quiet. At the sight of her tears, my eyes welled up.

"I remember." Every night, we would go to the window at bedtime and blow him a kiss. I would picture him on the other side of the world, catching the kiss in his hands and holding it close to his heart.

We stared at the sky and cried.

"You were such a little thing ... only six years old ... and he was gone a long time."

"After a while, I could barely remember his face." I looked over at my mother, but she had gone back into the apartment. I could hear her moving the furniture around. I stepped closer to the balcony railing and lifted my upturned hand to my face. The wound on my wrist looked ugly and red. The skin was puckering up.

"I've never seen so much dust," my mother said. I followed her voice into the living room. She'd pushed the couch against the wall. "I should never leave the windows open."

Dust, we had learned in grade six science, was a potpourri of everything likely to be drifting around our home — animal dander, face powder, dead skin, hair, cigar ash — or any debris that might be blown in every time we opened the door or windows, including soil, pollen, insect excreta, and general industrial pollution. Was my father's body now reduced to ash and dust? Was it drifting into our apartment through the open balcony door, wanting to cling to our furniture, our clothes, our skin?

We were still in the living room, scrubbing, when we heard the lock turn. The front door opened.

"A hot bath and bed," my father said, as if speaking to himself. He stood in the door frame and took in the scene before him: the furniture pushed against the walls, the bucket and mop and cleaning supplies.

We stared. My mouth filled with hot, dry air that made my body light.

"*T'étais où?*" my mother asked, anger tingeing her voice.

My father took off his glasses and wiped his face with his hands. He shut the door behind him and leaned against it. "I got caught behind enemy lines. My partner wanted to go further, see what was behind the barricade. I've always suspected the French and Belgians were spies ... I never should have agreed to go so far ..."

"Guy Wilson came to the door and told us you were MIA," my mother snapped. "Everyone thought you were dead." She was scrubbing the television set as if it were filthy. "I don't have any supper to offer you."

"All I want is a bath." He was already headed to their bedroom, hallway candle in hand.

"I knew he was a fool," my mother said. She kicked the sofa back in place with her right foot.

I stood back and watched her, too tired to offer my help.

My chest felt heavy, and my wrist throbbed. I wondered who she was calling a fool: the pilot, the Belgian UN officer doubling as a spy, or my father ...

After a few minutes, I could hear the water running.

Then Daddy, in his bathrobe, came back in the living room. "We're out of hot water again."

"I know. I've been using cold water to clean."

"How could we run out again so soon? Someone must be siphoning our gas tank. I'll tell the concierge in the morning. This system isn't working for us."

"Not much is working." Maman set her rag aside and followed my father into the bedroom.

I blew out the candles in the living room and kitchen, then walked to my bedroom by sliding my hand along the wall in the dark. Maybe I would stumble along the way, knock something over, fall down. Maybe my parents and Etienne would come running out of their rooms to make sure I was okay, get me a glass of water, inspect my wounds.

But I found my way on my own, pulled back the covers from my bed, and let the night claim me.

Beirut downtown (near the Green Line), March 1983.

~

TRADING
PLACES

~

And when he awoke in the morning and looked
upon the wretchedness about him, his dream had
had its usual effect — it had intensified the
sordidness of his surroundings a thousandfold.

MARK TWAIN
THE PRINCE AND THE PAUPER

In French class one Friday, Sunita, the girl I usually sat with, showed me a magazine picture of an Indian princess in her royal regalia. She wore a tiara, a nose ring, and long, sparkly earrings with a matching necklace and bracelets. Her turquoise sari was trimmed in gold. A man in a tuxedo stood next to her.

"That's me with Président Mitterrand," Sunita said.

"What?" I grabbed the magazine and flipped to the cover. *Paris Match.* February 1983. "That's you?"

"I went to Paris with my father on a diplomatic visit last fall. This picture was taken at the gala on our last night."

"You look like a princess."

"My father is the viceroy of Pondicherry. It used to be a French colony — like Lebanon and Syria. We still have strong ties to France."

I thought of what my father had said, that all the French peacekeepers were spies. I considered Sunita's faded jeans and sweatshirt. "You look so normal."

"I am."

"Does anyone else know this about you?" If I hadn't been so jealous, I would have told her about how, when I was little, I'd imagined myself as a changeling, a princess baby who'd been given to my parents to hide me from a wicked uncle.

The bell rang, as if breaking the spell. Sunita gathered her books. "No one really cares," she said, but I'd read too many fairy tales to believe that could be true.

When I entered the English classroom, Mr. Turner was writing on the board.

Once all seven students were seated, he turned to face us. His good eye landed on each of us in turn, while his glass eye fixed on the map of America on the back wall. I was both fascinated and repulsed. Mr. Turner was grossly overweight and balding. The gelatinous flesh around his cheeks and neck jiggled when he spoke. Yet there was an elegance about him, an assurance I found comforting. I took refuge in his passion for the English language.

"Literature is powerful." His eye roamed the classroom and landed on me. "It can change us. Change the way we see the world." He reached for a paperback on his large wooden desk and held it up. "Mark Twain was an American and British novelist whose life straddled two continents and two centuries. *The Prince and the Pauper* is about identity and setting, both of which are of extreme interest to all of us, as expats."

Someone behind me snickered, but Mr. Turner carried on. "Identity speaks of the very essence of who we are. Setting speaks of time and place. Where do I come from? Where am I going? These are universal preoccupations." He paced the room.

"Who among us has ever dared to fantasize about switching places with another person?"

The hair on my arms stood at attention.

He distributed a book to each student. "This," he said, drawing a deep breath that came out as a wheeze, "is the ultimate story of rags to riches."

When he placed a book on my desk, his chubby hand lingered a moment. "Let this story lift you out of your circumstances. Let it transport you to another time, another place."

I kept my head down and stared at my leather pencil case. Could he tell that I felt numb inside, that I'd been counting the days before I could leave the chaos of Beirut and return to Canada? Did he suspect I'd been cutting myself?

"Enjoy," he said softly, then moved on to the next desk.

On the cover was a picture of a prince and a beggar. They

looked like identical twins. If he wasn't aware of my situation, Mr. Turner must certainly have known about Sunita's double life. What about the other kids in my class? What were their real stories? Why hadn't they returned to the safety of their own countries like so many other diplomats' children? Part of me wanted to find out, but another part wanted to pretend we were all normal teenagers going to high school.

At the end of the afternoon, I took the book home to read on the living room couch.

Maman had the TV on, and was listening to the BBC news. "Tension is escalating in the Bekaa Valley," the male newscaster said in a clipped, efficient voice. He could have used the same even tone to read his grocery list to his wife: *eggs, bread, milk, sausages, more fighting between the Sufi and the Christian militia.* The screen showed snow-capped mountains and a guerilla fighter in combat fatigues. In the background, there was a Lebanese flag with its tall cedar and red stripes.

When Maman went to the kitchen, Etienne changed the channel to an Arabic soap opera. He turned the volume off and made up his own words. "Ahmed, I can never marry you. My father simply will not allow it," he said in a high-pitched voice. Then, in a deep tenor, "Myriam, baby, let's run away together." He tossed a sofa cushion at me. "Your turn."

"Oh, Ahmed," I giggled. "It will never work out between us. We're finished." When he tried to grab me in an embrace, I bopped him on the head with another cushion. "You cheeky thing."

For a golden moment, it felt like we were small again,

playing good guys and bad guys in the living room. But then Etienne/Ahmed's arm circled around me and pulled my body in toward his. "Gotcha." I was close enough to see the dried skin around the pimple on the side of his mouth, the shiny zit head white with pus. The soft growth of fuzz above his upper lip. He held me long enough to prove himself the winner. But then the way he dropped me and walked to his room made me feel as if I were diseased, or smelled of B.O.

"Yoo-hoo, Ahmed," I called in a singsong voice outside his bedroom door. No answer. The game was over, just like that.

Maman had put some stamps on my bed. She must have come in and tidied up while I was at school, because the clothes I'd left on the floor were neatly folded on my chair and the bedcovers were pulled over my pillow.

I sat on the bed and examined the stamps. All Canadian. Snow falling on a *cabane à sucre* in a grove of maples; a winter rabbit; a large frontal of Queen Elizabeth with a green background; a lynx looking straight ahead, tail erect. Tonight, I would soak them in warm water until the stamps separated from their envelope papers. Then I'd dry them on a towel and place them between the pages of our huge family atlas. Tomorrow they'd be ready to be catalogued.

A wave of homesickness rose from my belly up to my throat and made my eyes itch with the threat of tears. If only I could switch places with someone, like the prince did with the beggar. I'd had the chance — I could be married by now and living in Damascus! But that wasn't the kind of life I wanted. My old classmates in Yellowknife would never believe me if I told them that story.

Maman knocked on my door, then opened it a crack. "Supper."

"What are we having?"

"*Gigot d'agneau*." Her smile looked forced.

"Again?"

"Lamb is all I can get."

My father brought two extra wine glasses to the table before sitting down at his spot. "Sunday, we're taking you shopping." He pulled the cork out of the bottle of white wine and poured us each a glass.

My mother raised her eyebrows. "*Pour les enfants aussi?*"

"They're old enough. I'd already left home at their age. And where else will we get good German wine for so cheap? Let them enjoy it." My father was in an unusually good mood. I wondered if he'd had a few glasses of sherry before the meal.

My mother frowned the way she did every time my father mentioned his boarding school years. Whenever Maman complained that he was asking too much or being too hard on us, he would remind her that when he was a teenager, he'd only come home for brief visits at Christmas and summer vacation, when he would work in the logging camps with his father to pay off his tuition.

"Can we get a boombox?" Etienne asked. Clearly, he'd also picked up on our father's good mood. I hoped he might wink at me and call me Myriam, but it was as if I wasn't even at the table.

"Yes," Daddy said. "You can each pick one out. And we'll get a video cassette player for the TV so you can watch American movies."

I was pleased but puzzled by my father's generosity. He was a frugal man; he didn't buy us gifts except on birthdays and Christmas. He insisted that we live within our means, according to his budget. Maybe he was trying to compensate for his prolonged absences and constant preoccupation since arriving in the Middle East. These days he came home to shower, eat, and sleep. The moment he woke up, he had the shortwave radio going in case of an eruption of fighting somewhere in the city. Maman must have reminded him he had a family and talked him into doing something with us.

"We have money up the ying-yang, for once. Isolation pay and a healthy expense account now that I'm operating officer." The alcohol seemed to have loosened him up, like the Tin Man in *The Wizard of Oz* once his rusty joints had been oiled. "This is the opposite of Canada. Cost of living is high, but electronics and jewelry are cheap."

"Black market?" Etienne suppressed a burp.

"Wine is meant to be sipped," my mother said. "Not slurped or guzzled like milk." Her face and voice reminded me of the time she'd caught my brother looking at a porn magazine in my uncle's bathroom.

"When we get to Canada," Etienne said, "I'm going to drink cold milk, right out of the fridge. No more fake boxed stuff."

My father refilled Etienne's wine glass. "In the animal kingdom, only babies drink their mother's milk. After your wine, you can have a Fanta."

When my mother looked down at her plate, Daddy snorted. "Sunday, I'll take you to the downtown area and the places where the locals shop. Show you a bit of Beirut you haven't seen yet." My throbbing head was already reacting to my father's version of the good life. I would have preferred to stay home and play a board game as a family.

Maman's head jerked up. "The old downtown? The Green Line? Next to the port? Is it safe?"

"Don't worry." My father reached for my untouched wine glass. "I know what I'm doing."

Sunday morning, we drove down Beirut's bombed-out boulevard along the Corniche, the pedestrian boardwalk that flanked the Mediterranean. I looked out at the garbage-strewn beach. A dead cow rode a wave, its bloated brown belly rising toward the grey sky. Below us, a man rolled up his pant legs as if he planned to wade into the sea.

"How can people picnic on the beach next to all that trash?" I asked.

My mother made a face. "*C'est dégoutant.* That water is full of disease."

Etienne yawned. "Where else is he supposed to swim? *Les Bains Militaires?*"

"Of course not," Maman snapped.

"Can we go to the pool today?" I loved eating pretzels on the outdoor deck at the *Bains Militaires.* The luxurious, gated compound with its shade trees and fancy waiters reserved for United Nations personnel and military attachés helped me forget about the devastation on the other side of the wall.

"Maybe after our shopping," Maman said.

My father manoeuvred the car into the opposite lane to avoid a massive hole surrounded by a pile of sandbags. "We're almost at the Green Line. The shops are on the other side." Our apartment was on the Muslim West Side, considered far safer. It was our first time crossing over into Christian East Beirut.

Etienne slumped in his seat and flicked on his pocket-sized Donkey Kong.

My father pulled the car over to the sidewalk, but we all remained inside. "There's the Maronite cathedral." The massive building had been heavily shelled, leaving pews and part of the altar exposed to the sky. Spray-painted graffiti covered its brass doors. "It's been looted — inside and out," my father continued. "Even the famous Delacroix painting of Saint George — Beirut's patron saint."

"*Quel dommage,*" Maman said. "Nothing is sacred here. Nothing escapes the war."

"Legend has it, this is where Saint George slayed the dragon," my father said in his storytelling voice. If I closed my eyes, I could pretend I was in front of the fireplace in our Yellowknife living room, listening to him read aloud to us. "Beirut was blockaded by a monster that terrorized the inhabitants. It demanded that the ruler hand over his only daughter in exchange for the city's peace."

I pressed the fresh cut on my left wrist, hidden under my long-sleeved sweater. A shiver of pain rippled up my arm and into my neck. "Did the ruler give her over?"

My brother smirked. "Of course."

"He did," my father said. "But as the princess left through the *Bab es-Serail* — the east gate — Saint George rescued her and killed the dragon."

I pressed the scar again, harder this time. It felt like a dragon could be lurking around the corner, ready to pounce. I'd just finished reading *The Hobbit;* my imagination was full of Smaug. Like the city of Esgaroth, Beirut had mountains in the north, where the PLO and Hezbollah had their training camps — dragons' lairs of weapons, machine-gun nests, and mischief.

"Maybe the city is cursed," Etienne mumbled. It wasn't hard to believe. Most of the buildings along the Green Line were severely damaged. Even the cross on the cathedral's roof was broken in two. It looked like it might topple at any moment.

"Are we going to Mass?" I asked.

Etienne rolled his eyes.

"No," my parents said at the same time.

"Terrorists target areas with lots of people," Maman said.

"Places of worship are dangerous," my father said. "The UN cautioned us not to go to church."

I pictured the inside of our Catholic church in Yellowknife, its pews full of Native people bused in from the reservations up north. Father Vachon preached his sermons in Dene and Dogrib while people listened or dozed off. There was comfort in the predictability of our priest's quiet ceremony, which he performed every Sunday regardless of whether there were ten people gathered for Mass or one hundred. I loved the pungent, musky smell of incense and wax mixed with the earthiness of chewed leather and tobacco. Every Sunday for the last three years, even in the Arctic winters of forty below, our family had bundled up and walked half an hour to St. Pat's on the edge of town.

It fascinated me to see my father kneel at the entrance to the pew, cross himself, and bow before the altar and the massive crucifix that hung from the ceiling on a heavy chain. We sat shoulder to shoulder and repeated the liturgy. Sit, stand, sing. Repeat. Eyes forward. My brother was an altar boy, a job reserved for his sex. I longed to know the mysteries of the small boxes and bells, the secrets contained in the locked cupboards in the sacristy, as exotic as the daydreams of angels. Once, Father Vachon explained that the church, with its ribbed wooden ceiling, was like a massive boat, a Noah's ark that would carry our families to safety over the floodwaters of evil.

But those memories were on the other side of my life, before my father had decided I'd spend my thirteenth year in the Middle East. My life was divided into two sections as clearly as the Green Line that separated East and West Beirut.

"This is the old city centre," my father said, once he'd resumed driving. Apartments and storefronts stared back at me through windows that looked like empty, black eye sockets. The haunted buildings were held up with sandbags and surrounded by barbed wire.

"Imagine," Maman said. "Beirut used to be called the Paris of the Middle East. Elegant and cosmopolitan. Now look at it. *Il n'y a plus personne.*"

"You'd be surprised how many people still live here," my father said. "Entire families. It takes a lot to make someone abandon their home."

I thought of our pink-panelled house on Gitzel Street in Yellowknife. My room on the third floor, with my desk and lamp in the corner, the bed where I'd read a thousand books. Who lived there now?

"There's a massive housing shortage in Beirut," my father said, "thanks to the war. We're lucky we found an apartment."

I'd heard my parents say this several times since our arrival in January — that we'd gotten one of the only apartments left — but instead of bringing me comfort, it made me wonder if our building might be the next one to get bombed.

I clutched *The Prince and the Pauper* in my lap, torn between my curiosity about this destroyed and deserted main square and my desire to escape it.

My father steered the Peugeot onto the cracked sidewalk and put it into park.

"What are you doing?" my mother asked when he opened the car door and got out. Her voice had a high, wobbly quality to it.

"I thought we could walk around," my father said. "Have a look at the place where the war began."

Maman scanned the ransacked buildings. "There could be snipers on the rooftops." Just the other day, a soldier had been killed while eating a hamburger at Wimpy's, my favourite restaurant on Hamra Street. He'd been sitting at a booth next to the window, in the section where Maman, Etienne, and I usually sat. The man who shot him had been stationed on a rooftop on the other side of the street.

"The fighting has shifted to the south side of the city," my father said. "We should be fine." When he slammed the door, a huge rat ran out from under a discarded mattress and darted across the street.

Daddy came around and opened the passenger door for my mother. She hesitated before getting out. "I'm dressed for shopping," she said. "These aren't walking shoes."

"Don't worry," he said. "I'll hold your arm."

I left my book behind and followed my parents and brother on the desolate street.

"Maybe this is where Doc Millington is hiding," I said. My father's colleague, a kindly Canadian man in his sixties who gave me stamps for my collection each time he came to dinner, had gone missing ten days ago.

"I still think he's been kidnapped," Etienne said. It was a common danger for foreign journalists, who were routinely held for ransom by terrorist groups. But in July, the threat had struck closer to home. David Dodge, the president of the American University of Beirut, had been kidnapped one evening while walking home across the campus. Dodge had been smuggled out of Beirut through Baalbek and was still being held in a prison in Tehran. What if the same thing happened to us? Etienne and I walked by the place where Dodge had been abducted every day on our way to school and back.

"I don't think Doc's been taken," my father said. "I think he ran away. Maybe to Cyprus."

"*Le pauvre.*" Maman had a soft spot for the middle-aged, unmarried medic who always complimented her profusely on her French-Canadian cooking. "He must have cracked under the pressure of living here."

I envied Doc Millington, wherever he was, even if he'd had a mental breakdown. He'd found a way to escape.

My parents stood beside a sapling that had pushed its way up between broken slabs of pavement on either side of the demarcation line. Maman pointed at a vine growing up the façade of a building. "Morning glory. It must be drinking the acid in the rust."

The street made me think of the scene in *Sleeping Beauty*, when Aurora is woken from the spell of her hundred-year sleep and her ruined castle has been transformed into a lush, green garden. On either side was destruction. But all along the line separating the city into Muslim west and Christian east, trees, shrubs, and wildflowers grew — an astonishing sight amidst all the ruin.

Etienne held his sleeve up to his nose. "It stinks like a cesspool. Let's get out of here."

"I want to take some pictures of us in Martyrs' Square." My father took the camera out of its leather case. "Gather together around the base of the statue."

My brother climbed up the sandbags and gave a military salute. His other hand rested on the ivory pedestal beneath the bronze figures towering above.

I bent to read the plaque at the statue's base, but it was riddled with bullet holes.

"It commemorates Lebanese and Arab nationalists, executed here in 1916," my father said. "By the Ottoman empire." He snapped a few pictures.

"Let me fix my hair," I said. But he'd already put the lens cap back on and was returning the camera to its case.

"It's not like we're going to frame these and put them on the wall." Etienne jumped down. "Why would we ever want to remember this place?"

"You'll look back on this year and be grateful." It was a stock phrase Maman served us periodically, the way mothers in Canada might serve shepherd's pie to their family every second Tuesday. She held a tissue up to her nose. Her eyes, like mine, were streaming from the acrid garbage smell.

The familiar numb feeling was coming back, like a hood over my emotions.

"Can we go shopping now?" Etienne asked.

"The store I have in mind is just around the corner, on the next street," Daddy said. "I patrol here often. I know the shopkeeper."

"I'd like to get some twenty-four Karat earrings and a microwave oven," Maman said. She had a jewelry box full of treasures from her travels with my father. She turned to face me. "How about you? Maybe a chain? Or a bracelet?"

I dropped my eyes to the broken sidewalk. I didn't want to have to lift my sleeve so the jeweller could measure my wrist or fasten the bracelet clasp. "I don't want any souvenirs."

Instead of shopping, I wanted to slip into a church, seek refuge — sanctuary — as if this were an ordinary Sunday in an ordinary place. I craved the atmosphere of quiet and peace I'd felt in St. Peter's on Christmas Eve, and how even the fishing boats bobbing on the lake outside had seemed to belong to the time of Jesus. I squinted my eyes, imagining the figure of a man in white walking toward me on the moonlit water, hands outstretched.

"*Salaam, salaam,* Major Don," called a bearded man in a nearby doorway.

My father waved, called out a greeting and strode ahead to join him.

Soon we were all standing in front of the bearded merchant. "Come in," he said in heavily accented English. "See what I have for you." He pointed to a backgammon board inlaid with mother of pearl on display in the dusty storefront window. A bullet had made a hole in the glass, surrounded by an elaborate network of lacy cracks radiating out from the broken middle like a spider's web. "We have coffee for you," the merchant said. "Friend price. Sunday special. Welcome. Come in."

Etienne and my mother eagerly followed my father. I hesitated on the sidewalk, reluctant to enter the claustrophobic shop with its cardboard boxes piled to the ceiling, but not wanting to be left alone on the sidewalk, either.

My father caught the door before it closed. "Come choose some earrings," he said, ushering me inside. "Or a necklace. Something beautiful you can bring back to Canada."

If I could have written the script, he would have slipped his arm around me or taken my hand in his. But instead, he led me to a glass cabinet with a polished countertop, where the bearded man was arranging his display of gold chains.

Outside the shop, car horns mixed with the muezzin's call to prayer.

On the way home, my brother and I cradled our new Sony boomboxes on our laps. We'd also bought some pirated ABBA, Air Supply, and Kiss tapes for me and Etienne, along with Chopin's polonaises and Dvorak's New World Symphony for Maman. We'd paid two American dollars apiece for the tapes instead of the usual $9.99 at home. I couldn't wait to set up the tape player in my room and listen to music on my bed.

"Can we stop for food?" Etienne asked.

"I'm not completely sure where we are," my father said. We'd taken a series of detours because of street barricades. He fiddled with the city map open on his lap.

"Are we still in a safe area?" My mother had the sun visor down and was admiring her new ruby earrings in the small mirror.

"Is any of it safe?" The question slipped out before I could stop it. I didn't want to dampen my father's mood. He was pleased with the deal we'd gotten on all our stuff. "A steal," he'd said when we'd left the shop.

We were interrupted by the blast of a car horn and the screech of metal on metal. We'd collided with another car.

The driver, a Lebanese man about my father's age, stood in the narrow street. He waved his arms and pointed at his broken headlight and smashed front fender while shouting in angry Arabic. My father stayed in the car and watched him. When he finally rolled down his window and stuck his head out, the man stopped shouting for a moment.

"My street." He made a pushing gesture with his hands, indicating to my father to back out. "I own road."

"I think he's trying to tell you it's a one-way," my mother said.

"It's a long way to drive in reverse." When my father looked in the rear-view mirror, our eyes locked. A thin line of blood stretched from his iris to the edge of his eyelid.

"Aren't you going to get out of the car and talk to him?" Etienne asked.

The man was still shouting and gesticulating. His old car was already banged up. There was a big crack down the windshield, and the left side mirror was attached with duct tape. The circular Mercedes-Benz symbol on the front hood was askew, broken at the base and dangling by a wire. Arabic disco music wafted in through the open car window and mixed with the driver's tirade.

"You guilt." The man brought his fist down on the hood of our car. "Stupid American."

To my surprise, my father remained silent. He reached into his pocket and handed the man a few Lebanese lira through the car window.

At that, the man calmed down and got back into his car. My father put the Peugeot into reverse and draped his arm over the seat so he could look behind us as he drove.

"Why did you let him treat you like that?" Etienne asked. "As if you'd done something wrong."

"He could have had a gun in his pocket and another tucked under his seat," my father said. In response to our stunned silence, he added, "It's not worth the argument. Why put the family at risk?"

I waited for my mother to say something, but she was fiddling with her earring's butterfly clasp.

"We should have a gun," Etienne said.

My father swerved the car to avoid a massive pothole. "UN peacekeepers are unarmed," he said. "You know that. It's the whole point."

"What about us? It's the weekend. You're not on duty." Etienne's eyes scanned my father's pockets, as if hoping to spot the butt of a revolver. He checked the two seat pockets in front of us, but all he came up with was a flattened box of tissues. "You must have a weapon of some sort. For self-defence."

"It's how he damaged his hearing," my mother said. She had been listening after all. "No earmuffs on the firing range. Too much assault on the eardrums."

My father lit a cigarette. "We're here to end the conflict. Not add to it." He had the same skin tone and hair colour as the cowboy on the Marlboro magazine ads and billboards all over the city, the same unsmiling but satisfied look as the rugged, outdoorsy man who reined in his horse or whipped a lasso around his head.

"Daddy," I said, as the smoke wafted into the back of the car. "Maybe you should think about quitting. To save your lungs."

"I'll quit in Canada." He said Canada the way Grandmaman said Heaven, what she called *le ciel*, the place where everything was pure, good, and right, and justice was served.

"How was your weekend?" Monsieur Thierry asked in French, once we were all seated in our classroom next to the library. "What did you do?" He was intent on having us exercise our

French conversational skills. He insisted on an answer from each student.

"I went shopping," I said when it was my turn. "And I watched TV." It was the answer any teenager at home in Canada might have supplied, not much different from what the other students had said. Even Sunita. But I wasn't sure I believed any of them. If it was that easy for me to lie, what about them? What were they still doing here, in Beirut, a theatre of war?

That was the question I wanted Monsieur Thierry to ask the other five students in the room, all from different countries. But he had moved on to French declensions, written in alternating yellow and white chalk. Next to me, Sunita bent over her notebook and copied the *passé simple* of *le verbe avoir* in loopy cursive, as if she were wholly engrossed in the lesson and had nothing to hide.

BEIRUT BOMBING

~

In Lebanon, nothing is surprising...
ISRAELI FOREIGN MINISTER YITZHAK SHAMIR
APRIL 1983

In the three months since our arrival in Beirut, we'd never gone out after dark. Around five, soon after the muezzin's call to prayer, the shelling would begin. We always heard it, even when it came from behind the mountains. At dusk, we pulled the heavy drapes across all our apartment windows as if they could protect us from the terrors of the night.

Still, I had to ask. "Maman, there's a Sadie Hawkins dance at school next Friday night." We were washing the supper dishes by candlelight in our apartment kitchen. Blackouts in the city were frequent.

"You're not going." She grabbed the frying pan with her gloved hands and leaned her weight into the sink to scrub.

"Please, Maman, everyone will be there. Can't you make an exception? Just this once?" My glasses were steaming up from the boiling water she'd just added to the sink. The city's septic system had mixed with the fresh water supply, and we needed to add ammonia or bleach to our bathing and washing water. The sharp, aggressive smell of the disinfectant made my eyes water. I turned my back to the sink to escape the odour and wait for my glasses to clear.

It was lonely for us, this business of staying inside, respecting the curfew. Our only outing was our daily walk to school and back. The compound that contained the university, embassy, and school was surrounded by a tall iron gate with two guards at the entrance. Each morning, we had to show them our identity cards with the school logo and our picture. Then the guards searched our schoolbags, even our lunches, and looked at us hard, as if we were potential criminals. But once we were inside the gate, the scary-looking guards outside made it feel like a safe place.

"What are they looking for?" I'd asked my father at supper time, a few days after we'd started at the school.

"Explosives," he said. "Weapons. Information. Smuggled goods."

"On me?"

"You might not be who you say you are," he said, lifting his wine glass. "To them, everyone's a suspect."

When his connections in the CIA and the Lebanese militia gave him inside information about what he called "hotspots" in the city, where violence was expected to erupt, he kept us home from school. It was his job to discover where the fighting would be, and then go there, as a United Nations presence, to bring peace.

But all I could think about was the dance.

"Ginnie said her father can come get us after the dance."

"The American helicopter pilot?" my mother asked.

"I could sleep over at their place." I held my breath. My mother splashed more boiling water into the sink. I peeked back at her. Beads of sweat dripped down from her forehead into the water.

"It's not safe. Foreigners get kidnapped at night. All kinds of things could happen."

"Maman, please. One night. Just this once. Everyone is going."

My mother paused. She wiped her face with the back of her gloved hand. "I know it's been hard for you here." She handed me the gleaming frying pan and reached for a stainless steel pot.

"I'll call you as soon as we get to Ginnie's."

She shook her head. "What if the phone lines are down?"

"Please, Maman!"

"I have to talk to your father. I can't promise you anything. I'm sorry."

"Can we at least go to Groovy's?" It was a European fashion boutique we'd found when we'd first scouted out the downtown.

My mother turned to look at me. In the candlelight, her pupils were enlarged, her face soft.

"It's my first high school dance," I said.

"I know."

"I saw a purple miniskirt in the window last time we were on Hamra Street."

"*On verra*," she said, "we'll see."

The next day was Saturday. We sat across from each other at a small round table in a pastry shop in downtown Beirut. "This place reminds me of *la rue Sainte-Catherine* in Montreal." Maman smoothed the linen tablecloth. "*Deux chocolatines, s'il vous plaît*," she called to the pastry chef who doubled as waiter. We watched him use silver tongs to extract two croissants from the display case. "I love all these Old World details, all these *gâteries*," she said. "*Apportez-moi votre meilleur thé*," she added when he placed the pastries before us.

I held the bag from Groovy's in my lap. My mother had agreed to the skirt and even suggested I buy stockings to match. I was relieved and elated that she understood the importance of the outfit — how everything hinged on fitting in.

She sipped her tea from a tiny porcelain cup without handles. "In the gardens of Sri Lanka," she said, "only virgin girls are allowed to harvest the white tea blossoms used to make this tea. They use golden scissors and golden bowls." She held her teacup with both hands in front of her like a sacred object. "To this day, they continue the same practices as in the time of the aristocracy, when white tea was reserved for Chinese royalty. Imagine that!" she said, bringing her cup to her lips and resting it there. "I am drinking what an oriental empress would drink in the morning, in her private chambers. Does that link my destiny with hers somehow?"

I looked quizzically at her face, then down at the straw sticking out of my Coke can. "If the fighting gets worse, are we going home?" I asked her.

"Where is home?" she asked, staring into her teacup.

"Canada." How could she not know that? I had an instant headache.

"It's a big country." She pressed the fingers of her right hand down onto her plate to pick up the leftover croissant crumbs. "We're not going back to Yellowknife, if that's what you mean." She licked her fingers slowly, one at a time. I had never seen her do that in public.

"We can stay at Grandmaman's. Anywhere is better than here," I said, pointing out the window with my chin. An old Mercedes taxi, its passenger door held together with duct tape, honked its horn at a group of men in army fatigues. Their machine guns and ammunition belts bounced against their chests as they ran across the street. The car screeched to a halt to let them pass, then charged forward, muffler roaring.

"We're staying until your father has finished his work," my mother said into the teacup.

My father had told us about daily sniping against Lebanese civilians in Christian East Beirut. The UN presence was meant to stop the fighting. Sometimes it did, my father said, and sometimes it didn't.

I had never seen this side of my mother before: vulnerable, unsure of herself. Until now, she'd always been right there alongside my father, ready to follow him on his next adventure. But things were different here. The city was falling down around us.

Etienne had his own passport, but I didn't. I was an appendage of my mother, fully dependent. Where she went, I went. If she fell apart, so would I. It was a terrifying thought.

I sucked on my straw until it made a loud slurping sound. My mother made a face at me and reached for her purse. "Let's head back," she said.

As soon as we got home, I laid my new outfit on the bed for closer inspection. It was perfect. Short purple skirt gathered at the waist, striped stockings that made my legs look funky and long. It was artsy and sophisticated, and I loved it. I thought Richie, the Australian boy in grade eight, would like it too. I brought the cotton skirt and stockings up to my nose and breathed in the cloying chemical smell of new clothes, then stretched out on my bed and turned my thoughts to Richie.

"I can see your bra through the back of your shirt," he had whispered to me under the big maple in the school compound the day before. It was the only mature tree in our part of the city. All the others had been cut down or ruined by the war. I liked leaning against the huge trunk and looking up at the sky through its branches.

"You're sexy," Richie continued.

My face, neck, and arms pulsed with instant heat. I hadn't realized my shirt was transparent at the back. Why hadn't Maman told me before I'd left the apartment that morning? Hadn't she noticed?

"You remind me of Brooke Shields in *The Blue Lagoon*."
Richie leaned his arm on the trunk of the tree behind me,
and brought his face close to mine. I could smell the sweat
on his skin.

I turned to look at the kids walking by on their way to
class. A few stared. I wondered vaguely if my brother could
see me, or if they'd report to him what his sister was up to
under the big tree. But then the bell rang, announcing the
beginning of classes, and I was saved from Richie's hot breath
too close to my neck.

At school that Monday, I sat in the library after lunch. My
grade seven class was in the basement for band practice, but
I had a free period. Since I'd only started at the school in
January and didn't play a band instrument, I was exempted
from music class. I spent my free time on the top floor in the
reading lounge, next to Mr. Thierry's classroom. After that, I
would study advanced French while my class did beginner,
baby French in our regular classroom downstairs. At dinner
time at home, I took perverse pleasure in imitating the way
they counted to ten with their thick accents.

Suddenly, there was a deafening boom, a sound louder
than I'd ever heard before. Everything shook. The room went
black. Books fell off the shelves. The chairs next to me rolled
over. A window cracked and split, sending shards flying.

After the huge sound of the blast, there was a thick quiet.
I sat alone in the darkened library, assessing the damage.

What just happened? Was it an earthquake? What should I do?

A light shone around me. "*C'est l'heure du français,*" Monsieur Thierry announced. I stood up, eyes blinking, and followed his flashlight beam into the classroom adjacent to the library. For the next hour, we conjugated French verbs by candlelight. "*Que je puisse, que tu puisses.*" Monsieur Thierry's lips pushed forward when he spoke, as if all the words were teetering on the edge of his mouth, ready to dribble out. I thought of Richie and how *puisse* sounded like the English word *kiss*.

Whether Monsieur Thierry had forgotten about the blast that had just shaken our school or decided that his curriculum was more important, we carried on covering the board with our white-chalked declensions made visible by the candles on the teacher's desk and the shafts of faint afternoon light coming in from the upper casement windows.

We were a small group, our numbers at the American Community School greatly reduced by both the civil war and the war with Israel. As tensions in the city escalated, most diplomats packed up their families and returned to their own countries. The only new influx of expats to the city were fifteen hundred U.S. Marines sent by President Reagan to man the five U.S. warships anchored a few kilometres offshore.

After Advanced French, I joined my class on the first floor for grade seven English. Mr. Turner examined us with his one good eye, while his glass eye stared straight ahead. Its fixed look unnerved me. It was like staring at a camera. I imagined it photographing my secret thoughts — a bionic eye with special powers.

"A bomb has exploded nearby, at the American Embassy," Mr. Turner informed the class once we had taken our seats. "Fortunately for us, our school remains unscathed." He paused, but only for a breath. "Please take out your copies of Twain's *The Prince and the Pauper*. We will read aloud, beginning at Chapter Three."

My hands picked up the paperback and flipped mechanically to the correct page while my mind wrestled to process this new information. I raised my hand. "How close did we come to being hit?"

Mr. Turner's glass eye stared at a distant spot behind my head while his good eye looked out the window. "We'll find out soon enough," he said.

It was a relief to get lost in the story of a faraway place and forget about what was going on in the city around us.

"Be careful on the way home," Mr. Turner said before dismissing the class for the day. "See you tomorrow."

Our regular route through the campus was blocked off by red tape marked DANGER. We were shepherded into two lines and made to show our identity cards and hand our schoolbags over for inspection by armed French military police at three different makeshift checkpoints inside the gate, before finally being given permission to exit onto the street. Sirens blared nearby, and traffic on the main street was barred. The empty street was an eerie sight compared to the usual noisy tangle of cars and pedestrians.

My brother walked a few paces ahead of me. "Did you hear it?" I asked him. I watched the back of his head nod yes.

"I was in art," he mumbled. It was hard to hear from behind. I got as close to him as I could, but the passage was only wide enough to walk single file.

"We left class and went there." He stepped onto the street to avoid a pile of garbage on the sidewalk. In the absence of waste removal services, the citizens of Beirut piled their garbage in huge stinking mounds on the sidewalk. Those nearest to the beach threw it into the Mediterranean. After almost ten years of anarchy and civil war, the city resembled a massive dump.

"What do you mean? Where did you go?" Our school never went on field trips of any kind; it was too dangerous to leave the gated compound.

"Mrs. Gunthrey wanted to see what had happened. Her husband works at the embassy, and she needed to make sure he was all right. So she took us there."

"Was he okay?" I kicked at an empty sardine can, shuffling it back and forth between my feet like a soccer ball.

"Took a while, but we found him. He was all white. Covered in dust. He thought his arm might be broken. He was holding onto a woman whose face was cut up. Her eyes were full of blood."

After that, my brother was quiet for a long time. I kept my head down and followed his footsteps exactly, walking in the street to sidestep more garbage and a car parked on the sidewalk, also a common occurrence in this city without traffic lights or police surveillance.

"I saw a car wrapped around a telephone pole," my brother said in a voice so low I thought maybe I hadn't heard him properly.

"What? How?"

"It's the force of the blast," he said. "It picks up anything in its way."

When we got home, Maman was frantic. She called to us from the balcony. *"Enfin!"* she said, raising her hands into the air. In her white dress, she reminded me of our old Catholic priest in his vestments, raising his arms to say the blessing over the communion bread and wine. "You're safe!" She disappeared through the open kitchen door, the heavy drapes shutting her from sight. Moments later, she was on the street trying to hug us both at the same time. *"Mon Dieu!"* she said. *"Mon Dieu!"* She caressed my braid, running her hands up and down its length.

She leaned her shoulder into our front door as she turned the key in the lock. *"Aidez-moi,"* she said. The bulletproof leather made the door extremely heavy. "A few more minutes and I was coming after you." Her hands fluttered up to her face, then to her dishevelled hair.

It occurred to me that maybe she'd been afraid to leave the apartment to come looking for us. Maybe that was why she never met us after school or walked us there or back. I had no idea what she did all day while we were at school and my father was working. I knew she spent time with a few of the Canadian officers' wives: Sharon Windsor and Violette Vaillancourt — Ghyslain's wife — but that was all. She was always waiting for us when we arrived, cooking something up for our dinner, eager for news of how the day had gone.

"Come, sit, I made you some *chocolat chaud,*" she said. "Tell me what happened."

I had nothing to say, beyond my experience in the library. My brother drank his cocoa in a few quick draughts. His face was tight and strained as if he hadn't slept in a long time. He didn't tell our mother what he'd told me, just went to his room and shut the door.

"The radio says there are many dead," my mother said. She burst into tears, then jumped up from the couch. "I need to contact your father. I need to tell him you're home. Safe." She grabbed the telephone on its stand in the hallway, held it to her ear, then slammed it back down. "No connection." She continued trying, then slid down onto the sofa and remained there, crumpled up. She tried to smooth her skirt over her knees but then slumped her shoulders over, as if exhausted by the effort.

"I heard the blast from over here. I knew it was something big. There was footage on BBC-TV … I saw people lying in the street outside your compound. I have no way to reach your father at *le quartier général*. I tried calling the school, but *le téléphone était mort, comme d'habitude*." She started to cry again. She stared at the television screen, where a reporter with a British accent stood in front of a demolished building.

When my father finally came home around seven that night, she was wild. "*On sort d'ici!*" she shrieked. She was still wearing the white summery dress, but it was wrinkled and limp, like a paper napkin. Her hair had come loose on one side, while the other was still pinned up, giving her an unbalanced look. Pin in hand, she tried to coax her thick hair into its twist, but it kept falling back around her face.

My father sat down on the sofa and fiddled with the transistor radio on the coffee table. "We'll go to Greece for a couple of weeks," he said, "until the city calms down. We'll visit Athens, like you've always wanted — see the Acropolis. From there, we can go to one of the islands. Whichever one you want: Mykonos, Rhodes, Crete. You decide. It's time we took a holiday."

It was enough to quiet my mother. She stopped pacing and came to sit near him.

"But we can't leave for another week." He adjusted the radio dial.

My mother left the couch and stormed into the kitchen. *"Tout de suite!"* she shouted. *"J'en peux plus!"*

"I have work to do in the city. Especially after what's just happened. It took us all by surprise. Even our contacts in the CIA. At least one of them is dead now, maybe two. We've lost our best American sources.

"I'm commanding officer," he continued. "You can't expect me to leave after this disaster. It will take us a week to sort it all out. After that, we can go. We don't even know who's to blame."

"You are to blame," my mother shouted, her angry face framed by the kitchen doorway.

Still holding the buzzing radio, my father walked to their bedroom and shut the door.

Next morning, he wouldn't let us go to school. "It will be a zoo down there," he said. "They're still searching for bodies."

BBC News set the death toll at sixty-three. Over half were Lebanese embassy employees; seventeen were Americans. The rest, unnamed, were bystanders. An additional 120 or so were wounded.

"How could a car bomb kill so many people?" I asked.

"It was a delivery van packed with two thousand pounds of explosives parked at the very front of the building," my brother said. "A suicide bomber."

That night, I woke from a deep sleep to the hellish sound of my brother screaming. His cries pierced the apartment. The hallway light was on, and my parents' bedroom door was open.

My father stood in the hallway, holding his burgundy bathrobe closed with his hand. One end of the terry cloth belt hung loosely from his side. The rest of the belt trailed behind him. *"Fais quelque chose,"* he said to my mother. Do something. I could hear the sound of her sobbing mixed with my brother's. I wondered what else my brother had seen that day that he hadn't told me about.

My father went to the storage closet in the brightly lit hallway and pulled out a pale yellow suitcase with one hand while he held his bathrobe with the other. After a few minutes, four suitcases lined the hall. He turned to look at me. I was sitting up in bed, chin resting on my knees. Should I tell him what my brother had told me?

"Yesterday ..." I began.

"Find your bathing suit," my father said. "We're going to Greece."

"Skipping school?" I asked. "For how long?" But he had followed my mother into my brother's darkened room.

"There will be other dances," Maman said the next morning. She was cooking eggs at the stove.

"Yes," I said, "but this is a Sadie Hawkins dance. The girls ask the boys." I hoped to appeal to her sense of women's rights.

"It must be an American thing," she said dismissively. She lifted her flipper and brought it down — *smack!* — against the counter, then whacked it again hard, then harder still.

"Maman, qu'est-ce que tu fais?" I asked. She brought the spatula down one more time and the thing split apart, the metal front and screws clattering to the floor. With the wooden handle left in her hand, she pointed at the spot where she'd been hammering. I picked up a crushed cockroach the size of my index finger, its grotesque body completely flattened by my mother's manic energy. I threw it over the balcony railing.

It was a final affront. When she put my father's plate in front of him at the table, her hands were shaking. "It could have been one of us out there, walking by the embassy," she said. She was still standing by the table in her bathrobe. My father's eggs were getting cold. I wasn't sure what to do. Should I start eating? Sitting down at the table together to eat was a non-negotiable aspect of our family. My father, who liked to eat his food hot, was always served last. Once he had his plate, the rest of us would begin to eat. I picked up my fork. I was hungry, but I was also scared of my mother. I had never seen her this angry.

"Our children could have been killed while sitting at their school desks. We can't go on like this."

My father held the pepper shaker over his eggs. "Please sit down."

But my mother refused. "They don't want us here, organizing their city for them, working for peace." She spat out her last word like it was something rancid.

My father started eating.

"The Greek resorts are all closed in April," my mother said. "It's too cold to swim in the Mediterranean."

"We'll rent a jeep in Crete," my father said, "and drive up into the mountains. The orchards will be full of fruit." He took a sip of his coffee. "I know people who can get us through the airport."

"What are you saying?" my mother asked. Her hands gripped the back of the chair.

"There's a possibility it may soon be under siege. It's a good time to take a little holiday." My father lifted the *Egyptian Daily News* so that his face was hidden behind the front page.

"I'm running a bath." Maman got up from the table and headed for the bathroom. I rifled through the pile of newspapers beside my father, looking for the comics section.

When she emerged a half hour later, her hair was pinned up, and she wore a fresh dress. It was a relief to see her put back together. In her hand were drawings pulled from a sketchbook. "I went into Etienne's room, to check on him and gather up his laundry," she said woodenly. "I found these on his desk." She held them out to my father, who was still seated next to me at the dining room table, surrounded by dirty dishes and headlines. She didn't realize my brother had followed her out of his room and was standing behind her.

"Hey," he said, reaching for his drawings, "those are mine." He looked like he'd slept in his jeans, and his eyes were sunken into his head. He grabbed the papers, but my father refused to let go. I leaned over his arm to see. There was an eyeball that was also a picture of the Earth, with its continents and oceans drawn in coloured pencil behind the pupil and iris. To the side of the globe, a large wound gaped open, with blood spurting out and dripping off the page.

My father lifted the corner of the page to see what was underneath. There, my brother had drawn people lying on their backs, their faces distorted into screaming holes. Under them were other bodies, mangled and twisted into strange positions. Blood everywhere. Over the nightmarish scene hovered a huge pair of disembodied eyes, partly obscured by cumulus clouds.

"You had no right to come into my room like that," my brother said.

My father placed the drawings face down on the table beside the *Jerusalem Post*.

"At the back of the fridge," he said, "in a cookie tin, are ten thousand U.S. dollars. If ever the fighting gets so bad that we need to leave in a hurry, and the airport is closed, we'll use the money to hire a rowboat to take us across the Mediterranean. I want you both to know that," he said, looking me full in the face. "Just in case."

Beirut Downtown.

RIPE

"Would you tell me, please, which way I ought to go from here?"
—Alice
"That depends a good deal on where you want to get to."
— The Cheshire Cat

LEWIS CARROLL
ALICE'S ADVENTURES IN WONDERLAND

After the embassy bombing on April 18, nothing in Beirut was the same. The next time my brother and I went to school, there was a massive tank parked outside the gates.

In English class, Mr. Turner told us his government was sending thousands more U.S. Marines to Beirut in response to this new threat. The chaos of heat and garbage, the noisy press of people, and the destruction felt increasingly oppressive. I longed for wide, peaceful spaces: fields, beaches, forests, even the white, frozen expanse of Great Slave Lake.

At recess, I stared across the bay at the American warships with their cannons aimed at the city.

"They're bringing Bob Hope onto the ships to entertain the soldiers." Ginnie did a perfect cartwheel on the asphalt walkway, then wiped her hands on her thighs and cartwheeled back to me. Her tight jeans accentuated her childish figure — slim-hipped and flat-chested, even though she was thirteen, a year older than me. She was half-Laotian, half-American, with her mother's petite build.

"My father is going to fly him in by helicopter. He's also got American magazines for the soldiers: *Life* and *People* and *Newsweek*." She lowered her voice and leaned into my ear. "And *Playboy*." She giggled, then looked me squarely in the face.

I tried to laugh and look sophisticated to mask my fear and confusion. I pictured the magazines stacked next to piles of ammunition and .45-calibre pistols. The summer before, when my uncle in Québec made a habit of leaving his *Penthouse* magazines open to their centerpieces in the middle of his bathroom floor, I'd felt violated and ashamed. I'd wondered why my mother and aunt hadn't insisted he put them away, at least during our visit. I had trouble looking at him at breakfast.

In the Middle East, I'd gotten used to avoiding eye contact with men. They considered me exotic, with my blonde hair and blue eyes, but their stares made me squirm.

"Twelve is considered the perfect marrying age," my mother had told me when I complained about it. "Enjoy the attention." We were walking down Hamra Street, shopping for shoes. "Men don't look my way anymore. They consider me past my prime. But you're ripe for the picking." She'd smiled at me in an admiring way. It terrified me to think of myself as fruit ready to be torn from its branch. I wanted to hide under a black burqa, like many of the women on the street, and become invisible.

"Do you think your Mr. Higgins will enjoy those girlie mags?" Ginnie asked. Her question startled me back to the present. "Were you dreaming about Billy-boy?"

My cheeks flushed red at the thought of Billy Higgins, the short stocky U.S. Marine from Virginia, studying a centrefold.

When I hesitated, she continued, "Maybe he'll come over to your place again tonight." Ginnie understood the ways of the world. Her mother, she said, told her *everything*. "Maybe Higgins will fall in love with you the way my dad fell for my mom in Laos. He was far away from home. My grandpa was an important military leader — kind of like your dad."

"He probably thinks I'm way too young."

"My mom was still a teenager when she met my dad." Ginnie arched her back effortlessly, then dropped down into a back bend. She blinked at me from between her arms.

"That's different," I said, wishing I could move my body like she did. I stood stiffly, feeling awkward, and shifted my weight from one foot to the other. "That was Laos."

"Why not here?" Ginnie straightened up, then tightened her ponytail, tucking in a few stray strands of hair that had come loose with her gymnastics. "My dad says anything can happen in Beirut."

"Let's go to the art room and work on our collages before

class." There were too many other kids milling around. I didn't want them to overhear or repeat this conversation to Richie Marks, who'd taken to calling himself my boyfriend even though we hadn't even kissed.

Ginnie walked beside me with the usual spring to her step. "Which theme did you choose for your collage?"

"Identity. You?"

"Satisfaction." She turned another cartwheel on the small strip of grass in front of the school building.

I wondered which images she would use to represent her theme. Nothing in me felt satisfied. I tried to remember the taste of ice cream with chocolate sauce and bananas, but lately I'd lost my appetite.

That night, as Ginnie had predicted, some of Daddy's colleagues gathered in our apartment. It had become an unofficial command base since the attack on the American ambassador. Among the men were Billy Higgins and Captain LaCroix, a redhead from Manitoba who brutalized the pronunciation of his French name into "Lacroy." I was attracted by Billy, the quiet young Marine, who I guessed to be in his early twenties, and repulsed by the older soldier, a sarcastic know-it-all with hairy red knuckles.

Our suitcases, packed for our holiday in Greece, were lined up in the front hallway. We'd filled them in the middle of the night, after the bombing, in case we needed to evacuate the city. But a week had gone by and we were still waiting for official United Nations approval for my dad to leave Lebanon. I wanted to retrieve my favourite sweatshirt as well as the extra novel I'd packed for the trip. I fiddled with the zipper of my suitcase. It seemed to be snagged on something inside. I took my time trying to fix it. That way, I could linger near Higgins and listen to him talk in his thick Virginian accent.

"Home cooking," Captain Lacroix said when my mother came out of the kitchen in her apron. "My mouth waters at the thought. What kind of feast have you prepared for us this time?"

Maman smoothed her apron. "New Zealand lamb." She looked pleased at the captain's compliment.

"You don't buy your meat at the local markets, do you?"

"I wouldn't dare," my mother said. "I get it frozen. From Smitties."

"Wise woman. The major is a lucky man."

My mother and Captain Lacroix smiled at each other. I looked at my father, but he was absorbed in conversation with Ghyslain and Billy.

My mother's reputation as an exceptional cook was firmly established in my father's circle. We were seeing more and more of these men, yet less of Etienne, who had retreated to his room since the day of the bombing. Aside from school, he only came out for quick visits to the bathroom and kitchen. Tonight, he'd opted to eat at his desk, claiming a headache and a long day of classes.

"I brought some wine." Lacroix pulled two brown bottles out of a paper bag. "German white. I believe the *Liebfraumilch* is your favourite, Frau Bellehumeur?"

"Excellent," my mother said.

"Did you know it translates to 'beloved lady's milk?'" The captain winked at me, acknowledging my listening presence. I'd left the suitcases and stepped closer to them, so that we formed a triangle. Brown hairs protruded from his pockmarked nose. I wanted my mother to kick him out. I couldn't believe she was even talking to him. If this were happening at school, it would be classified as a full-on flirt. I could name two steady couples in the senior grades who had broken up over less.

"We'll have your wine with the cheese plate." My mother took the bottles from him and turned toward the kitchen. She gestured for me to follow.

Once inside the door, she consulted the handwritten menu she'd taped to the fridge. "Check the shrimp in the sink," she said without looking at me. "If they're still frozen, run water over them. But not tap water!" she added, just as my hand reached for the faucet. "You'll contaminate them." Even after months in Beirut, I still couldn't break the habit of reaching for the tap to brush my teeth, get a drink, rinse an apple.

"Maman, he was leading you on," I said as I knocked ice cubes into the sink.

"He's just lonely for a woman's company," she said. "When you're done with those, you can peel the avocados for the entrée."

"I don't know how to do that."

Maman sighed. "I'll do it. You can polish the silverware." She handed me a cloth. "Make it shine."

"What's the occasion?"

"No occasion." Maman sliced into the avocados' dark skin. "These men are hungry for a good meal. Higgins and Lacroix are single. No families. I thought we'd put a little sparkle in their lives. Entertain them."

"Like Bob Hope on the American warships?" I tap-danced across the kitchen.

Maman joined me in a fancy two-step. She was reaching out to draw me into a waltz when the oven timer started beeping. She ran over to turn it off, then grabbed her oven mitts.

"It's important to your father that my dinner turns out well." She poked a meat thermometer into the lamb roast. This had become her new identity: the major's French-Canadian wife. Good cook. Pretty and vivacious. I pictured what her collage would look like if she were part of the grade seven art class. Food and frilly aprons. Beautifully set tables cut from the pages of the *Canadian Living* magazines the government sent us each month.

When I was older, I had no intention of being dependent on a man, or having to reinvent myself each time his job moved him to a new part of the world. I wasn't going to be someone else's glorified servant. I would be in full control of my life. Not dependent on anyone. A writer had no need of husband or children. I could see my collage in my head. It would be covered with books and pencils, a typewriter, and a calligraphy pen. Tonight, after the guests had left, I would hunt through the fresh stack of magazines we'd just gotten, and cut out the images and words I needed. I was relieved we didn't have any of the girlie magazines Ginnie's father delivered to the U.S. Marines tucked in amongst our pile of *Maclean's*, *People*, and *Chatelaine*. My father must have declined the offer.

At dinner, I watched Billy Higgins. He was quiet, deferring to the older men. When he rolled up the sleeves of his army fatigues, I could see muscular forearms with bulging veins and the edge of a tattoo — what looked like a woman's slender foot and ankle, but could also have been a spider's leg or an octopus's arm. My father had said Higgins was rigorously trained for theatres of war, with a West Point education. Part of the American military élite. He ate everything on his plate, then slid a piece of bread around with his fork until all the gravy was gone and the plate looked almost clean. He refused the wine, though the other adults were drinking with abandon.

"It was delicious," he said, when I cleared his plate. "Thank you."

I could feel the pulse in my temple and in the wrist above the hand that held his plate. I was close enough to smell his aftershave and see the blond stubble on his chin. I looked at his forearm to see if there was writing under the tattoo, a woman's name perhaps, but he'd unrolled his sleeves.

"You're welcome," I said, even though I hadn't done anything to contribute to the meal. I wanted him to think that maybe I'd made some of it, that I was older than I looked, and skilled in the kitchen, like my mother.

"Sure doesn't compare to the crap they serve us on the ship," he said. The adults around the table laughed. But I was too shy to say anything and scuttled off to the kitchen, holding his plate in my hand like a prize. When I came back to the table with the Queen Elizabeth cake, the men were talking loudly.

"Terrorist Narrative 101," my father was saying, "is that the Americans want to control the Middle East."

"Each country has its mythology," Lacroix said. "Don't we all have lies we cling to? Things we want to believe about each other, even though we know they probably aren't true?" He opened a pack of cigarettes and passed them around the table.

"Higgins," Lacroix continued, "what did they teach you about terrorist mythologies at West Point?"

"The enemy is real," Higgins said, refusing the proffered cigarette pack. "The threat is real. They taught us to defend our nation's freedom whatever the cost."

My mother lifted the serrated knife above the cake. "Who wants it plain, and who would like whipped cream?"

"Remember the rest of us, stuck here in this hellhole while you're lounging half-naked on a beach in Greece," Captain Lacroix said to me when I came back from the kitchen holding the cheese plate in one hand and a basket of grapes in the other. I felt my face go red and hoped he wouldn't notice. He plucked a large grape from the basket and popped it in his mouth.

"You should work on your tan while you're there," he said with his mouth full. "You're pretty pale." While I busied myself wiping crumbs off the embroidered tablecloth, he rattled on. "Did you hear about the French-Canadian man on his way to Old Orchard, Maine? He stopped a passer-by on the side of the road and asked him where he could find a beautiful bitch. Get it?" Lacroix snorted and smacked the table. My father chuckled. "A bitch instead of a beach," Lacroix said to Billy Higgins, who was looking at him blankly.

"Are we still going to Greece? When are we leaving?" I asked my father. But if he heard my question, he chose to ignore it.

"The major told me you're leaving in a couple of days," Lacroix said. "I'm driving you to the airport on Saturday morning. Who knows? Maybe I'll hop on the plane with you."

The stink of the cheese was suddenly unbearable. "I have homework," I said, turning towards my room.

My mother was handing out new wineglasses so everyone could switch from red wine to white. "*Il faudra que tu m'aides avec la vaisselle*," she said.

The captain snorted. "Dishes. *La vaisselle*. My grand-mother was a Métis who spoke French and Algonquin. I can give you a hand in the kitchen, Lucie, if your girl is too busy with schoolwork."

My father glanced up from his conversation.

"That won't be necessary." My mother filled the captain's cup. "I can always get Etienne to help."

That night, after the guests had left, I heard my parents' voices escalating into argument in the bedroom next to my mine. I couldn't make out their words. Part of me wanted to press my ear against the wall, but I turned on my music instead. I wanted them to respect my need for privacy; I figured I should respect theirs.

Past midnight, Etienne, whose nightmares had been getting steadily worse, started screaming again. I lay in bed, listening. After several minutes, his panicked cries increased. How could my parents not hear him? I knocked on their bedroom door. No response. I put my hand on the doorknob and turned.

The first thing I noticed in my parents' darkened room was the smell. It was new to me: thick and pungent, tangy, yet slightly sweet. Two tangled bodies were writhing on an untidy bed. A noisy ceiling fan spun overhead. It took me a moment to take in the scene and realize what I was interrupting.

I backed up, hoping they hadn't seen me. But when I'd opened the door, I'd let in light from the hallway, as well as the sound of my brother's cries.

"Give us a minute," my father said loudly over the screaming. I retreated to the safety of my room, longing for the anesthesia of sleep.

Outside the Beirut International Airport in April, 1983,
en route for our holiday in Greece.

~

JOURNEY

~

*All journeys have secret destinations of which
the traveller is unaware.*

MARTIN BUBER
THE LEGEND OF THE BAAL-SHEM

We're finally gone, I wrote on a clean, white page in my journal as our plane taxied away from Beirut. My mother's excitement about Greece had rubbed off on me. No more civil war. No more chaos and stress. I planned to chronicle and document each aspect of our vacation.

But less than an hour after we arrived, the vacation was already going sideways. "Athens is dirtier than I'd imagined," Maman said. We'd left our luggage at the hotel and were walking toward the main square, which was covered in pigeons. A group of young men in ripped jeans and leather jackets came off a trolley bus across the street. One had blue-and-purple hair cut in a Mohawk. Another wore a black collar with metal spikes around his neck. A mangy dog limped beside them.

"But no piles of garbage here," I said. "And no one carrying a submachine gun." The punks looked like they might have knives slipped into their boots or pistols in their pockets, but I pushed that image out of my mind.

"Let's go to the National Archaeological Museum," Maman said.

My father nodded. "It should be in walking distance from here."

"I'm tired," said Etienne. "I want to go back to our room and watch TV. They might get some American shows here."

"We're in Greece," Maman said. "We need to see the sights. There's so much to learn. You may never be back here again."

"Maman," Etienne said. "I don't give a crap about the sights."

"Watch your language, young man," she snapped.

"It's fun doing something together — as a family," I said, hoping to make peace. I'd invested so much hope in this holiday.

My brother scowled, picked up a pebble, and threw it at the pigeons, making them scatter in a flurry, only to settle less than a metre away.

My father asked for directions from an older man in a knitted beret who was feeding popcorn to the birds. He answered in a long string of Greek explanations. Seeing the confusion on my parents' faces, he laughed, then pointed to the right of the parliament building. "*Ena*," he held up one finger: "*Panapistimion. Dio*," he held up two fingers: "*Omonia*."

"Didn't you study ancient Greek in seminary?" my mother

asked my father, once we'd resumed our walk, in search of Panapistimion Street.

"From priest to soldier," I said. "Quite the switch." I thought back to Immaculata and her tape recordings of the Pope's sermons. Was my father ever devout like that? He never spoke to us about his faith in God, but he made sure we were in church every Sunday.

"Let's hope it all comes back to me," he answered.

Mrs. Nouger would be so excited to know that I was visiting Athens, getting a "Real Education." Only ten months had gone by since I'd been sitting at my desk in the grade six classroom at Mildred Hall, watching her write on the board, waiting for recess to come so I could play with Catherine on the swings. But it felt like years.

By the time we got to the museum, I had a blister on my right foot. My shoes were too tight. I sank down on a bench in the immense foyer, blinking in the dim light, a sharp contrast to the strong Mediterranean sun outside. "I'll wait for you here."

"Nonsense," my mother said. "You can't miss this. We're like explorers, discovering new, uncharted territory." She was speaking in her overly cheerful voice, the one she'd used with her charges at the Yellowknife Playschool.

I was about to resist. But then Etienne called out, "Come look at this." He was standing in front of a life-size bronze statue of a naked man. "Poseidon," he said. "But with his eyes gouged out."

"Creepy." I was riveted by the empty sockets.

"It says here that they were originally inset with bone," my mother said before moving on to join my father in front of a statue of Aphrodite.

I wondered what had become of those eyes of bone. Had they rotted? The plaque at the base of the statue claimed that the sculpture had been fished out of the bay off the Cape of Artemision. The expression on the god's face was severe, devoid of all emotion except anger. His arms had lost their trident. The scholarly note pointed out how the arms were outstretched in a demonstration of strength, holding the potential for violence.

This powerless threat matched the opinion about God that I had formed over the course of our year in the Middle East, where both sides of the conflict claimed to fight in His name. But God remained impotent and silent — submerged by the conflict, like Poseidon, swallowed by the menacing sea over which he claimed to rule.

My mother came alongside me. "It will be our turn to head out to sea tomorrow," she said, "on our way to Crete."

Maman's forced cheer depressed me. I wished we could all just relax and be the way we used to be, back in Canada. I wanted to believe that would happen once we got to the beach. I looked up for one last glance at Poseidon's empty eyes.

The Greek gods intimidated me with their weird mix of sexuality and spirituality. Etienne stared at Poseidon's large genitalia, while my father stood uncomfortably close to Aphrodite's bare breast.

"Maman, why are they all naked?" I asked.

"They represent humanity at its finest — the perfected human body."

I felt a blush heat up my face.

"Love and war," my father said in front of the goddess Artemis. "What life is all about."

There was no way I wanted to talk to my parents about sex. But there were many things I wanted to ask them about war. My mind kept returning to the same stubborn questions. *What if the fighting in Beirut gets too bad for us to go back at the end of the week? What if our apartment is blown up while we're away? What if we don't fit in when we go back to Canada in July? What if we don't make it back alive?*

"Maman," I said, "what if the fi …" But she had turned the corner and was entering the precious jewels exhibit.

As soon as we arrived at our island resort, Maman and I realized we had both forgotten to pack our swimsuits.

"It's our off-season. Our shop is under renovation," the front desk clerk explained when we asked him if the hotel had any women's bathing suits for sale.

"Surely you have access to the shop's inventory," Maman insisted, flashing her most charming smile. "This is a guaranteed sale."

The balding, middle-aged man disappeared into a storage closet and returned with a small cardboard box, which he placed on the counter in front of us.

My mother pulled the top half of a burgundy string bikini

out of the box. "Perfect," she said, then rummaged through the box for the matching bottoms. What she pulled out was equally tiny. "Now for a second one," she said, and produced the two matching parts of a bright yellow suit.

"*Maman, je ne peux pas,*" I whispered.

She turned to me. "It's all there is." She smiled at the clerk, who was lingering close by, pretending to be busy with a paper and a stubby pencil. "These will do nicely."

Back in the hotel room, she laid both swimsuits on my bed. "Take your pick. Yellow or burgundy?"

"Maman, I can't," I pleaded. "I'll wear my jeans. I'll swim in shorts. I'll cover myself with a long T-shirt." I hadn't cut myself again, but I felt a loathing for my body. I didn't want to look at it, and I certainly didn't want anyone else to see it.

"We have limited clothing for the trip." My mother picked up the burgundy suit and held it out to me. "Just try it on. You'll look fantastic."

Etienne smirked from his spot on the small couch, where he was watching Looney Tunes in Greek.

I told him to shut up, even though he hadn't said anything.

Outside the window, the sun was shining on the Mediterranean. I wanted to sink my toes into the white sand of the beach, collect seashells, swim in the turquoise water. I grabbed the burgundy two-piece, stormed into the tiny bathroom, and slammed and locked the door.

"I'll go back down," Maman said, "and see if that disagreeable man can sell me a cover-up. He must have something."

She came back with a fringed pink T-shirt dress that was clingier than anything I'd ever worn. But at least it covered the bikini.

Next morning, Maman knocked on our door to wake us. "Get ready," she said, when we let her in. "Daddy has booked us on a boat tour to Gavdos Island."

"Why can't we just stay here?" Etienne grumbled, getting back into bed.

"Gavdos has the best beaches," my mother said. "Get dressed." She handed us each a granola bar and a juice box.

"But there's a beach right here," my brother protested.

The back-and-forth motion of the small boat as it crested the waves made me sick. I leaned my head against a pile of rope and tried to breathe in the salty air and focus on the intense blue of the water and sky, but my stomach roiled along with the sea.

"This better be worth it," Etienne mumbled beside me.

The moment we landed, his face lit up. The beach was covered in topless women.

"*Mon Dieu*," my mother said as we disembarked. "*Donne-moi tes lunettes.*" She tugged at my father's glasses. Like me, he was severely myopic. Without his glasses, he wouldn't be able to see a thing.

He stopped her hand. "What did you expect?" He chuckled. "This is a major European destination."

"You knew? And you didn't warn me?"

Etienne's eyes were bulging out of his face. He'd already spread his hotel towel on the sand. I just wanted to lie down and close my eyes to stop the constant swaying motion I still felt even though I was off the boat.

"No need to feel self-conscious about your bikini here," my mother whispered to me. "We'll be wearing twice as much as most of these women." She stretched out beside me. The yellow bikini bottom came just below her bulging abdomen. I reached out a finger to poke it. She was slim all over, but had always had that tummy fat.

"Baby residue," she said. "You'll have it too, one day."

I pulled my novel out of my backpack. I didn't want her saying anything else about my body.

"Aren't you going to swim?" my mother asked.

"Soon." But the truth was, I was too shy to parade in front of my father and brother wearing less than my underwear. I waited until they'd gone to buy drinks, then stripped down and made a dash for the water.

The rest of the afternoon, wearing my pink-fringed beach dress, I collected seashells along the island's western shore, away from the sun-worshipping crowd. The shells' unique forms and fragile beauty fascinated me.

The following days at our resort, I expected our family to do things together, like play shuffleboard or ping-pong or frisbee on the beach. My dad was an expert ping-pong player from his days at boarding school. Instead, we each took refuge in our solitary pursuits: reading, sunbathing, shell-collecting, TV. We came together for meals, but even then it was my parents who made conversation while my brother and I listened.

I collected seashells at every opportunity. I brought them up to my room and organized them in sections according to size, shape, and colour. The cataloguing made me feel like a field biologist or botanist making sense of the world around me. By the end of the week, I had hundreds of shells arranged on the carpet outside the bathroom. That spot had the most direct light, enabling me to study nuances in my collection: the crenellations, fossil-like imprints, and textures.

Some of the shells hosted living creatures. I could tell because the straight lines I'd made were moving, swaying as if in the wind.

"You're stinking up our room," Etienne complained.

I ran some water in the bottom of the bath and placed the living mollusks in there.

"What are you doing?" Etienne said. "You're crazy."

On our last day, my father announced he'd rented a jeep. "We'll drive around the countryside," he announced. The jeep was open to the air, with only a canvas covering. The wind pushed against our faces, sometimes even stealing our breath. Strapped into the back, across from my brother, I felt invigorated as we drove up the steep and narrow incline.

We drove all afternoon, taking in the view from the heights and observing how people lived. In grottoes tucked into the mountainside and in the gardens of people's homes were small shrines to the Virgin Mary. They were made of white stucco and created a rounded enclosure, like a bathtub turned on its side. I wondered who had lit the candles, and what they expected Mary to do for them. Standing there with her arms wide open or cradling an infant, she seemed as vulnerable and powerless to me as the blind Poseidon in the museum in Athens.

"Why do the Greeks worship Mary?" I asked Maman. We were walking around, stretching our legs. My father and Etienne had gone to the village store to buy cigarettes, bottled water, and chocolate bars.

"It's not worship. It's veneration." When she saw my blank expression, she continued, "More like a deep respect."

I nodded, even though I wasn't sure if I understood.

"Mary intercedes." She paused in front of a garden shrine. Mary's face looked like it had been freshly painted, while her blue robes were chipped. "The Virgin Mary presents your requests to God the Father on your behalf."

"You mean she pleads your case?" I asked.

"Yes."

I pictured God as a supreme judge in a heavenly courtroom. I couldn't approach Him on my own, but needed this lady to do it for me. But then, no surprise. I thought of all the times I'd gone to Maman first. I would discuss what I wanted with her, tell her why I needed it, and then, especially if there was a financial consideration, she would choose her moment to present it to my father. "It's all about timing," she would often say when I came to her.

This made Daddy sound like a live volcano. But I trusted Maman. She knew him better than anyone else. And there was no way I could confide my desires to my father. He didn't have time to listen to me. Even if he did, his initial answer was always no.

"Mary is spotless," my mother continued. "The perfect woman. The mother of us all."

Like Aphrodite, only better. I could see why people preferred to do business with Mary rather than the all-powerful God who was everywhere at all times and could see everything even though He, Himself, could not be seen. I always preferred to talk with women rather than men. It was easier, and less embarrassing.

In the village café where we stopped for dinner, a man was playing the guitar while another played the accordion. The tables had been pushed to the edges of the room. In the centre, men danced in a fast-moving ring, their arms about each other's shoulders. Women sat at the tables, cheering and clapping. We sipped on carbonated water and ate spanakopita while my father drank ouzo in a miniature glass that a waiter frequently refilled.

The men moved lithely, their arms like branches of a large tree swayed by the wind. They seemed absorbed by the music and by each other, dancing in unison, elegantly anticipating each change in tempo.

Without warning, the knot of men broke apart, and each dancer chose a female partner. The youngest dancer, a muscular man in his twenties covered in facial hair so thick that it blossomed out the top of his shirt collar, danced over to our table. He pulled my mother to her feet and led her to the centre of the floor.

"He's got hair in his ears," Etienne snickered. "And his pants are too tight."

"He'll be coming for you next," my father said to me. "You'd better get ready."

"Hairy as Sasquatch," Etienne continued.

"I won't go." A wave of anger rose up in me.

The man had one arm around my mother's shoulders while his other hand rested on the waistband of her thin summer dress. I didn't like the way he'd hooked his index finger through her belt. He was close enough to smell her breath, her perfume, the sweat and dust that clung to her skin.

A few of the dancers exchanged their partners for new ones. "You're next," my father repeated.

I shook my head no and busied myself with the fried potatoes in a basket on the table, carefully dipping each one in olive oil and balsamic vinegar before lifting it to my mouth. Couldn't my father see how repulsive all this was to me?

Now there were only three dancing couples on the floor. The rest were clapping their hands and watching. After a few more twirls, my mother's dancer led her back to our table, then held his hand out to me. Maman's face was flushed pink. A line of perspiration beaded her top lip.

My father leaned towards me. His breath smelled of ouzo. *"A ton tour de danser."*

"C'mon," my brother said. "Shake it. Pretend he's Richie Marks."

I cut my eyes at him. "No," I said. "I can't." This strange man was nothing like thirteen-year-old Richie.

My mother was breathing rapidly, sitting next to me. She wiped her face with my father's pocket handkerchief. The man was still waiting, his hand outstretched in my direction. His bushy eyebrows met in the middle, creating one long line above his eyes. His white shirt was damp, and smelled of body odour.

The thought of this man holding me close to his chest, putting his hot hands on my waist and breathing into my hair while my father and brother looked on made me want to vomit.

The man began to turn away, but my father thrust out the palm of his hand, asking him to stop.

"Donald," my mother said in the voice she used when my father had had too much to drink.

But he would not relent. "If you dance with him, I'll buy you those embroidered doilies for sale by the door."

"You're paying her to dance with him?" Etienne asked.

I felt as though I'd been turned to wood, like a puppet.

By this time a few more dancers had come to our table. One of them tugged on my chair. Before I knew it, I was standing, then being swept into a tight embrace, then held at the end of a muscular arm.

The noise of clapping, music, and talking around me increased. The room spun. My legs were frozen in place, an anchor to keep me from losing control or crashing to the floor. I searched the smoky crowd for my parents' table, and finally saw my father's tall head, the shape of his moustache.

He was looking at me, but there were black, empty sockets in place of eyes.

The dancer tried to prompt me to move, but I couldn't. Another woman stepped up, a tourist who'd come in with a busload of other women, all American. The woman broke into what looked like a Highland fling, all ankles and knees, wrong for the accordion music. The man let go of me so that we could both watch. Her crowd of friends cheered and clapped all the way through her performance until she collapsed into a chair and demanded a rum and Coke in a loud, laughing voice.

"To Gail!" one woman shouted, raising her glass, and the other women followed. Soon the whole restaurant was shouting "To Gail!" Even my father had his glass raised, despite my parents' distaste for loud American tourists. My mother was not in her seat.

I slid back into my spot at the table. I couldn't stop the tears dripping down my cheeks. I felt humiliated and betrayed. For all the times I had wanted my father to notice me, I now wanted to be invisible.

"What's wrong with you?" Etienne rolled his eyes. "It's just a dance."

"I'd like to see you get up there in front of everyone," I said.

"I'm not a girl."

I searched my father's face for signs of anger or disappointment, but it was impassive. His fingers drummed against his glass of ouzo.

"I hate you," I said. "I hate all of you."

I rushed to the bathroom and locked myself into the

small, windowless room, then splashed cold water on my face and wiped it with the paper towel on the side of the sink. I stayed in there for a long time, head resting on my knees on the lowered toilet seat, until an insistent rap startled me. There was nothing to do but slowly make my way back to the table.

A small pile of embroidered doilies sat at my spot.

"These will make wonderful keepsakes," Maman said when I sat down. My father ignored me. Etienne was asleep, his head resting on his crossed arms.

"They'll look pretty in your new room in Canada." She rolled them in tissue paper and placed them inside a delicate paper bag.

Outside the café, she handed me the bag, but I refused to take it. I didn't want anything that would remind me of this night.

"Fathers just want to show off their daughters," my mother said. She put the bag into her purse and climbed into the jeep. "You can't blame him."

"I don't want to be shown off. That's the last thing I want."

I thought of the dancing bear I'd seen once at a street fair in Quebec City, its snout pierced with an iron ring, forced to stand on its hind legs because its front legs were broken. Its owner prodded it with a stick, coaxing it to dance, while another man played a mandolin. My father had given me a coin to throw into a tattered hat on the pavement, but I'd slipped the coin into my pocket when his head was turned.

"I thought you loved animals," I said once we'd crossed the busy street.

"I do," he said. But before I could press him further, a man in stilts selling cotton candy came ambling by. It was only hours later, at home in bed, that my questions came back to me, but by then it was too late to get any answers.

When it came time to pack, I wrapped my shell collection in the small garbage bags the cleaning lady left in our wastepaper baskets each day. I'd been putting them aside for this purpose.

"You can't bring all those home with you," Etienne said, when I started stuffing the bags in my suitcase.

"Why not?" I wrapped a dirty T-shirt around a bag of delicate, pale pink shells.

"They'll stop you at customs," Etienne said. "Countries don't allow travellers to bring in animals or plants from foreign places. In case of contamination. That's what they told us when we were getting ready for the Scout Jamboree in New Zealand."

"You think the Lebanese care about a few seashells invading their country?"

Etienne turned back to his cartoons. He had barely spent any time on the beach. Instead, he watched the screen for hours a day, no matter what was playing, or if it was in English or Greek. His posture and face were trancelike, as if his spirit had been transported into another world and only his body remained.

"I'll pack your clothes for you if you let me use space in your suitcase," I offered.

I took his silence as a yes. I was sure he'd be happy not to have to pick up all his dirty clothes.

"Don't remind me," Etienne said, still staring at the screen. "Tomorrow, we go back to hell."

My father and I in Greece, April 1983

WITNESS

For the dead and the living, we must bear witness.

ELIE WIESEL

"I'm taking you to Sabra and Shatila," my father announced one evening a week after our return from Greece.

Etienne didn't look up from his pocket-sized Mario Bros. game. "I'll stay home."

"We can't leave you here." Maman walked out of the kitchen, rubbing moisturizing lotion into her hands. She frequently complained about the caustic effect of cleaning products on her skin.

"I'm fourteen." Etienne crossed his arms over his chest. "If the power goes out, I can handle it." His skin had gotten worse in Greece; the pimple on his forehead looked about to pop, greasy with pus. "You stay here alone all day. Why can't I?"

"Nighttime is different. Much more dangerous." Maman

turned to Daddy, as if Etienne's defiance had jumped onto her. "*Pourquoi tu nous emmenes là?* You told us never to go out at night."

"I want you to see the kind of work I do," my father said. "To understand why we're here." He curled his moustache in the hall mirror and applied a bit of wax to the ends.

"I'm not sure about this." Maman rubbed her hands as if trying to remove a stain from the surface of her skin.

Etienne left his device on the couch and set his school bag on the dining room table. "I have two chapters to read for history homework."

Daddy spoke to Etienne's reflection in the mirror. "I'm going to show you a piece of recent history." He handed my brother a jean jacket from the hook by the door. Only it wasn't Etienne's, it was mine.

Etienne shoved the coat aside but didn't unzip his schoolbag. "I hate field trips."

Maman hesitated in front of the boot rack, reaching first for her knee-high leather boots, then for her pumps.

"You won't be getting out of the vehicle," my father said. "It doesn't matter what you wear on your feet."

We climbed aboard the white UN jeep parked outside our apartment building. I was excited about driving in my father's work vehicle, under the Mediterranean stars. It felt like we were on important, official business.

Daddy played with the car radio and set it to a French news channel.

While we drove through the city, I rolled the names of the places we were going on my tongue: Sabra and Shatila.

Maybe we'd have ice cream there, or French pastries, or the sweet Middle Eastern figs we'd had in Israel.

We drove through the downtown area near our school, fragrant with fresh-baked bread, cumin, and the delectable smell of roasting meat. Then the city lights lessened and disappeared as we entered a blackout zone. The streets got narrower, with more rubble and destruction. Piles of rotting garbage towered above the jeep. We covered our faces to blot out the stench of open drains. I felt the excitement drain out of me like air out of a bicycle tire.

My father turned down the radio a notch and cleared his throat. "In June, when Israel invaded Lebanon, their goal was to destroy or severely diminish the PLO — especially Arafat, their leader, who was living here. The Sabra neighbourhood was hit hard."

I tried to focus on his words, but they were getting mixed with the French weather report that buzzed in the background. "*Températures stables toute la semaine* President Gemayel assassinated *entre 24 et 27 degrés* ceasefire agreement *un minimum de précipitation* Phalangist allies *de fortes bourrasques en début de soirée* Lebanese Christian Maronite allies ..."

We went through a military checkpoint, where my father and the guard greeted each other with a curt nod of familiarity. Further in, the jeep stopped beside a hill of dirt that rose out of nowhere. It was hard to see in the dark. All I could pick out were the outlines of makeshift houses, their open doorframes and windows blackened by the night. In the distance, I could hear a dog barking and a thin, persistent siren wail.

"*Nous voici,*" said my father. "Shatila, the Palestinian refugee camp. I patrol around here every few days."

"It's so quiet. As if there's no one here." Etienne's voice wobbled and caught on the last word so that it came out as a question, pitching upwards like a dried leaf swept up by a rough wind. "What's going on? Where is everybody?"

"Until last fall, there were between three thousand and eight thousand people living here. Hard to tell how many exactly, since they're undocumented. But for three days — September 16th to 18th — terrorists came into the camp and killed everyone: elders, women, children. Even infants."

"Who did it?" I asked in a whisper.

"Some say the Phalange, some say Hezbollah," my father answered. "Perhaps as payback for murdering Bachir Gemayel — the President of Lebanon and commander of the Lebanese military. He was a senior member of the Phalangist party. The international community blames Ariel Sharon, since the IDF let the terrorists into the camps and didn't do anything to stop the massacre." He gestured toward the hill beside us. "They piled the bodies up with bulldozers and then threw dirt over them."

"*Mon Dieu!*" Maman covered her mouth with her hand.

I stared hard at the mound. I wanted it to be a mountain of dirt at a construction site instead of a mass grave. The small UN flag next to the radio antenna flapped in the night breeze. The radio announcer's voice droned on in fancy French. It sounded just like my father's voice: clipped and clean and distant.

My father drove slowly past the mound, onto the deserted village street. We peered into the empty cinder-block buildings covered with graffiti and splattered blood. A solitary man butchered a chicken on a table lit by a kerosene lamp.

"A handful of people live here now, like ghosts," my father said, "where before there would have been almost as many as in Yellowknife."

We were like the figurines in the Montreal wax museum Hall of Horrors we'd visited for my twelfth birthday. Staring forward with one expression.

"It's hard to imagine the four of us getting settled into our new apartment in Israel while all of this was taking place," Maman said.

"Shit." Etienne picked at a thread on the knee of his jeans.

Maman put her hand on his leg. "*Arrête*. You'll make a hole."

My father put the car in reverse, and we headed back toward the city lights.

"Why would anyone do this?" I thought of the IDF soldiers I'd seen every day in Tiberias — at the grocery store, in line for the bus, sipping a cappuccino at an outdoor café. Had they been part of this? Had Efrat's brother? "Why did they have to kill all the kids?"

"Deep hatred is like that." Maman looked at my father; he had his eyes fixed on the road ahead. It had started to rain, and the windshield was fogging up. "But did we really have to see it?"

"Someone has to," my father said.

The hole in Etienne's jeans was big enough to fit two fingers. Soon his knee would poke through.

We drove on the Corniche, where the Windsors and

the Vaillancourts lived in apartments that looked out over the sea. Most of the trees that had once lined the esplanade were broken in half or reduced to ragged stumps. Only a few remained intact, their branches bent towards the pavement. The wind off the sea pushed against the vehicle and made it sway. The air was clammy and cold; in spite of the tightly closed windows, the damp reached into the jeep and penetrated my thin T-shirt. In my excitement, I'd forgotten to grab my jean jacket from the dining room table where Etienne had left it.

"Brad and Sharon are finally getting their baby." Maman turned to me over the back of her seat. "She called me today." Her voice sounded funny, a mixture of anger and longing.

"Boy or girl?" The words came out on their own — an automatic response.

"*Un petit garçon.* What they wanted. They're calling him Sami."

"Where does he come from?" I felt like I was underwater, with pressure building in my ears.

"Apparently there's a convent near one of the other camps — the Little Sisters of Charity ... They shelter young women ... offer them refuge ... help them to give birth and find homes for their babies." She wiped the windshield with her hand, removing the fog in ever widening circles.

"That makes no sense." My father gripped the steering wheel as the jeep hit a pothole and jerked to the side. "They already have kids from their first marriages," he continued when he'd gotten the vehicle back into the right lane.

"Their first *few* marriages." Maman wiped the windshield more vigorously.

"Don't you think Brad is too old?" I asked. He and Sharon liked to call themselves The Newlyweds, but his skin was grey and wrinkled from chain-smoking, and he was the only man I knew who wore a wig.

Maman bit her lower lip. I worried that if she kept looking at me over her seat back she'd develop a torticollis like she'd had several times in Canada. "People do crazy things in war zones."

No response from my father.

My teeth had started chattering, but there was one more question I had to ask. "Why don't the pregnant girls' families help them with their babies?" It seemed so extreme to have to give them away to strangers.

"The baby might have been conceived through rape. During the Sabra-Shatila massacre. It's complicated." Maman leaned back onto the headrest and closed her eyes.

But nothing was impossible for Brad and Sharon, I thought as we left the sea behind. Even when their cat, Kissa, smuggled out of Israel, had fallen nine flights from their apartment balcony the month before, he'd landed on the roof of a parked car and survived the fall, all limbs and organs intact.

The junked out, rusted Mercedes on the sidewalk, cannibalized for parts, was my indication that we were almost home. My teeth were chattering wildly now. I had to keep my hand under my chin and grip my jaw shut to stop them.

"When do they take possession?" My father parked the jeep next to the new flowerbed that Mahmoud, our concierge, had planted while we were on holiday in Greece.

"It's not a new house. It's a baby," Maman said. "They get him tomorrow."

As soon as I climbed out behind her, I noticed the blackout. Every window of our apartment building was dark.

"I'm not ready to go back up yet. I need to gaze on something beautiful for a moment." Maman crouched next to the yellow, orange, and pink flowers that bordered the walkway. "It's fascinating how these flowers close up at night, to protect themselves from night-time nectar thieves like bats and moths."

"Who bothers to plant things in a war zone?" Etienne scoffed.

"Perennials are a symbol of survival." Maman struggled to straighten up. "They come up year after year." After she called for him to help, my father extended his arm and pulled her upright.

"We had tulips and crocuses in our garden in Yellowknife. Remember?" She shook the dirt off her boots. "They were the first flowers to come up, in mid June. No matter how harsh the winter had been."

My father held the front door open for her.

When she saw me in the foyer's emergency light, trembling with cold, all the optimism drained out of her face. "We need to get you into a hot bath."

"Mahmoud told me our tank is empty." My father's eyes flicked over to the basement stairs leading to the concierge's door and the row of oil tanks that held the supply for each apartment. "I'm sure someone is siphoning our oil," he whispered. "I've paid to have our tank filled three times since January. And the winter wasn't even that cold."

"Skin tax," Etienne said.

We felt our way up the stairs in the dark.

After almost five months, we knew the blackout drill: flashlight on the boot rack by the door, matches in the small drawer of the telephone stand, candles on the dining room table.

Etienne dropped onto the couch, making the frame creak. "No TV. I hate this place."

If I could have talked, I would have asked my father to read to us. In Yellowknife, whenever he was in the mood, my father would invite us to sit on the ottoman in front of his favourite stuffed chair while he read aloud from *Treasure Island*, making a spooky voice when it was Long John Silver's turn to speak. It was better than watching *The Muppet Show*, *The Love Boat*, or even *Charlie's Angels*.

But he was already heading down the hallway. "Early to bed," he said. Most days, he was up at four to be at his peace-keeping post before dawn.

"You take us to the site of a genocide, and now you expect us to drift off and enjoy sweet dreams?" Maman wrapped me in a knitted afghan and rubbed the space between my shoulders. "No power and no gas. Neighbours who steal from us."

I was getting carpet burn on my back from the strength of her rubbing. I would have asked her to stop, but my teeth were making a racket.

Maman wasn't finished. "You seem to have forgotten we have children here. What were you thinking?"

My father paused in front of the door to the master bedroom. "You should have said something sooner."

"I agree," Maman said. "Much sooner."

My mother's tone scared me. On the one hand, I enjoyed the way she was choosing me over him. It was what I'd been craving. But she was my ship and my harbour wrapped in one. I needed her to remain steady. If she crumbled under the pressure, so would I.

Candle in hand, Maman guided me toward my room and into my bed. She zipped me into a green army sleeping bag and tucked my blankets over top. *"Je suis vraiment désolée.* This is supposed to keep you warm in minus-forty temperatures — the biggest threat Canada has to offer."

It sounded like she was apologizing for the sleeping bag, which smelled like a sour combination of body odour and mothballs. But I knew there was more to it than that. It was the closest she could bring herself to saying that she and Daddy had made a big mistake.

Although my parents had often lectured me and Etienne about fire safety and the hazards of leaving candles unattended, Maman lit the cedar-scented pillar candle on my bedside table. "A night light," she said, kissing me on the forehead, "to keep you company."

I tried to close my eyes, but I kept seeing the desecrated settlement, the mass grave. After a long time, I fell asleep and dreamed of an empty-armed young woman wandering the alleyways between the cinder-block houses, calling the name of her lost child. But instead of Sami, it was my name she spoke into the darkness.

294

"The baby's birthday is April 18th," Maman said the next morning. She was curled up on the couch with her knitting basket, pattern, and yellow wool spread out around her. Daddy had left before the rest of us had gotten up for breakfast. The drama of the night before seemed forgotten. "He was born on the day the American Embassy was bombed."

"Will you get to see him?" I wished I could stay with her instead of having to walk an hour through the streets of Beirut to go to school. "Could I go with you?" I didn't really care for babies, but it was worth a try.

"You've missed too much school already."

What would I tell Ginnie if she asked me what I'd done the night before? *We went on a family outing. My father decided to take us on a tour of a few Beirut neighbourhoods.* No. I'd tell her the news about Baby Sami instead. *Our Canadian friends bought themselves a baby on the black market.*

It played in my head like a movie as I walked single file behind Etienne. Opening scene: Camera pans our school campus, the university, and finally the embassy. Caption on the bottom of the screen: *April 18, 1983.* Voice-over: *While a suicide bomber was planning his entrance onto the campus of the American Embassy with a hundred pounds of explosives in the back of his delivery truck and plans to assassinate the ambassador, a baby boy was born in a convent on the edge of a Palestinian camp in a suburb of Beirut.*

Cut. Something more dramatic: Intercut between a baby coming into the world as the driver detonates the bomb by driving straight through the delivery doors. Voice-over:

As seventy-two lives were violently extinguished in central Beirut, a small life was beginning in a southern slum.

But the story started even before that. Rewind to an earlier scene. Let the viewer see two separate tableaux happening simultaneously, split screen. On the right, a driver loads up his truck with explosives. He says his final goodbyes to his wife and children. Drives away. Left: a mother and her newborn baby see each other for the first time. They are still saying hello when a nun comes from behind and takes the baby out of the mother's arms. Bye-bye, baby.

Next screenshot: Our family and the Windsors in Canada, with cartoon speech bubbles, each saying the same word: *Hello.* If Sharon and Brad's plan was successful, they would obtain all the papers that would enable them to take Baby Sami out of the country to a new life in Toronto. In a few months, he would be one of us.

"*Americanboyhowareyou?*" The unfamiliar voice with fuzzy Arabic undertones — as if the speaker had been drinking too much Lebanese wine — smashed into the movie scenes I'd been splicing in my head. I stepped into the street so that I could stand beside my brother.

A man on a motorcycle barred the sidewalk. Acne-pocked face. Black leather head kerchief. Both ears pierced with a dozen rings and studs. On the Harley's handlebars, yellowed fingernails so long they curled. Knuckle tattoos in spidery Arabic script. The man killed the engine. He opened his mouth and wiggled his tongue at my brother. "*AmericanboyIhavesomethingtoshowyou.*"

Etienne stepped behind me into the busy street. When

he bumped my backpack, I was wrenched sideways. My sneaker squashed something soft as I stepped into a pile of wet garbage.

The man kept pace with Etienne by moving his motorcycle forward with his feet.

Morning rush-hour traffic whipped by in every direction. My father had designed this particular route to school so we wouldn't have to cross any main boulevards. Beirut streets had no stop signs or street lights, no police presence or traffic control. Getting to the other side unscathed at this hour was tricky.

We kept on walking.

"*Babyboy*," the man said. "*Comewithme.*"

We were almost at the university when Etienne stopped and turned to the man. "Leave me alone!" he shouted, then ran for the tank and military guard at the front of the gates. I followed, running as fast as I could.

We showed our school ID, had our bags searched, and slipped behind the safety of the locked gate.

"We have to tell Daddy." I had to jog to keep up with my brother.

"What do you think he's going to do about it? Stop us from going to school? You want to stay in that apartment all day, watching Arabic soap operas?"

"Maybe someone could walk us to school."

"I don't need a babysitter." Etienne pushed through the doors to the gym, where the ninth-grade boys liked to shoot baskets before the morning bell.

297

Talk at supper that night was all about the baby. It was just the three of us — Daddy had been called back to UN headquarters because of a security crisis on the Israeli border.

"Sharon asked me to be the godmother." Maman was as excited as if it were her baby.

I felt mildly jealous, as if this baby might lay claim to a part of my mother denied to me. But alongside that irrational fear came guilt and shame. I had to be crazy to resent an innocent baby rescued from a refugee camp.

A few weeks later, we stood together at the christening party.

"Have some champagne." A woman I didn't know handed me a long-stemmed, narrow glass from her tray. I looked around to gauge my parents' reaction, but neither one of them was paying me any attention. As for Etienne, he'd talked his way out of the reception at Brad and Sharon's on the claim that he had a Molière play to read for French class the next day. My father was part of a cluster of men in military uniforms of various shades of khaki. They stood around a beaming Brad, dressed in his navy whites. My mother was holding the baby while Sharon photographed her. I held the glass up to my mouth. The bubbles tickled my lip and gave off a fruity smell. Thirsty, I emptied the glass in one gulp, then walked over to my mother and Sharon.

"He was handed to us in an alley behind the convent," Sharon said. She adjusted my mother's knitted yellow blanket under the baby's chin. "The nun claimed Sami's mother was an unwed teenager. Her father and brother could kill her, you know." She scrutinized me under her bushy, unnaturally black bangs.

Suddenly light-headed, I leaned against my mother's shoulder to steady myself, but Maman shrugged me off. "*J'ai le bébé*," she said. "*Vas t'asseoir.*"

I looked around for a place to sit, but the chairs were all taken.

The baby winced in his sleep. "We paid an exorbitant amount of money for him," Sharon continued. "The nun called it a donation to the convent. Highly illegal, I think. But now we're a real family," she continued. "When we go back to Toronto, he'll learn French. And play the violin. Our own little Palestinian baby," she cooed, while her cat, Kissa, rubbed against her silk-stockinged leg and purred.

POSTED

...There never was a good War, or a bad Peace.

BENJAMIN FRANKLIN
LETTER TO QUINCY, 11 SEPTEMBER 1783

One afternoon in May, when I got home from school, Maman
had five large, military-issue cardboard boxes open in the
living room. She wrote OTTAWA ONTARIO in permanent
marker on both sides of each box, then handed me a roll of
packing tape. "Help me secure the bottom so nothing can
fall out. I'm putting the new VCR and microwave in here, and
they're heavy."

Maman polished a smudge on the large microwave oven
with the end of her sleeve. I helped her lift it and place it in
the bottom of the packing box. "Wait until Reine and Gisèle
see this," she said. "I'll be the envy of all the officers' wives."

"Do you know lots of people in Ottawa?" The hardest thing
about moving was making new friends. But Claire would be

in Kanata — not far away. I hoped we could be best friends again, like we'd been in grade three.

"We have lots of friends there. Ottawa is where most officers finish their careers. It will be the first posting where I'll feel like I'm part of a community the moment I arrive." She numbered the box, then wrote its contents in the corresponding column on her clipboard. "We might even buy a house. Imagine," she said. "After seventeen years of moving around — our very own home."

I smiled up at her. It was hard for me to get excited about an oven and a house, but it was nice to see my mother looking so happy.

"Maman," I said, wanting to take advantage of her good mood, "Ginnie and I would like to spend some extra time together before school finishes and we have to say goodbye for good." I paused to gauge her reaction.

She continued reinforcing the bottom of the boxes with packing tape. "What do you have in mind?"

I could tell from her voice that I would have to tread carefully. "Ginnie and her mom and dad are going to the mountains this weekend — to a resort with a pool — and they've invited me to come along."

"Absolutely not. *Il n'y a aucune façon* ... To Jounieh? *Non, non, non.*" The piece of packing tape she'd been handling bunched up. She tried to unravel it, but it knotted up even more. "What a mess." Maman threw the matted ball of tape and the permanent marker onto the coffee table. "Forget it."

I grabbed my schoolbag and headed to my room. "I'm sick of it here," I shouted. "I hate being cooped up all the time."

"Only a bit more than a month to go," Maman said. On the first of May, she'd fastened the calendar pages for May and June onto the fridge. Each day, she made a big X to mark our progress. On the June page, she'd indicated the last day of school and written CYPRUS across the seven squares in the middle, with a big sunshine and a happy face drawn in, followed by CANADA! and a large, lopsided maple leaf.

"Jounieh?" my dad said at supper. "There's talk of heavy shelling there this weekend."

I pushed my rice around on my plate.

"Besides," Daddy added, "Ginnie's father is on the UN's list of questionable people in Beirut."

"What do you mean?" I asked.

"He may be a mercenary. No one really knows."

"His car has Lebanese plates," my mother added. "He's not a diplomat or a government worker, or he would have been repatriated by now."

"You think he's a spy?" Etienne asked.

"Probably," my father said.

"One thing is for certain," my mother said. "He's not one of us."

I pushed my plate away. "He's Ginnie's dad. That's all that matters to me."

The next day, at afternoon recess, Ginnie and I sat underneath the big maple tree in the centre of the school compound. The roar of a low-flying helicopter sounded overhead. I was relieved to see it was a private chopper and not a military one. "That might be your dad," I said when the noise subsided.

"He's got lots of work these days," Ginnie said, "carrying supplies and people in and out of Beirut. Lots more if the airport closes down. He calls the war his bread and butter."

"I hate the war." Apart from having to say goodbye to Ginnie, I couldn't wait to leave Beirut for good. I was terrified to think of the airport going under siege and our family being forced to stay.

Ginnie picked up a two-lobed helicopter seed and let it drop to the ground. The place where we were sitting was covered with them. "My dad says the war in Laos was good to him too, since that's how he met my mom."

"Don't you want to go back to the States?" I asked. "To your real home?" I couldn't understand Ginnie's relaxed view of the war.

She glanced down at the Preamble to the American Constitution we were supposed to have memorized for our third-period history class, then dug the heel of her sneaker into the ground next to one of the tree roots. "We don't have a home to go back to." She gathered more helicopter seeds and set them in motion around her. "My grandparents don't like my mom. They nicknamed her the Chintz, even though she's Laotian, not Chinese. Last time we visited, they called her a whore and a bitch, and Mom said she'd never go back."

I couldn't imagine Grandmaman saying those words. "But what if the bombing gets worse?" I asked. "Where will you go?" The blackout had just lifted after three days of intense shelling.

"My dad has connections in the mountains," Ginnie said. "They tell him when to take a little holiday."

"My dad has connections too," I said. "Intelligence agents who know stuff ahead of time — like where the roadblocks will be, what parts of the city to avoid and when."

"Maybe they have the same connections."

I thought back to what my dad had said about Ginnie's dad. "Maybe," I said, wishing it could be true.

"Ginnie's father is a fool," my father said at supper time, when I related our conversation to my family. "The way this war is headed, every Lebanese family with two cents to its name has an evacuation plan. The U.S., French, and Canadian embassies are overrun with visa applications."

"I was at the Canadian embassy today," my mother said, "with Sharon and the baby. It was a zoo."

"Did they give you priority?" Etienne asked. "Since you're Canadian?"

"I still had to wait." She sighed. There was always lots of waiting in Beirut, with traffic jams and lineups everywhere.

"It's different there now that all the actual Canadians are gone," my mother continued. "All the embassy personnel are Lebanese."

"Why aren't we being sent home?" I asked.

Etienne scraped his fork across his plate. "What she means is, why aren't we leaving this hellhole like everyone else?"

"It's different for us." My father reached for the wine bottle that my parents had taken to putting directly on the table. "We're not civilians. We're military."

"You're military," Etienne looked at Maman and me. "The rest of us are civilians."

"Then please be civil," my father said. No one laughed at his cleverness.

For a few minutes, we ate our meal in silence. Then Maman extended her empty wine glass to my father. "At least we have options."

We'd all seen the Palestinian refugees jammed into their overcrowded camps and the Lebanese kids my age who'd grown up with the civil war raging around them. But we had ten grand in the cookie tin at the back of the fridge, and the Canadian passports hidden in the bottom of the laundry hamper in the bathroom.

"It's not quite what we expected, is it?" Maman continued. "A far cry from Nahariya by the sea and hobnobbing with the other expats."

My father chewed his food slowly, the way I did in Yellowknife when my braces had just been tightened.

"The Canadian embassy won't take responsibility for us." The second glass of wine was making my mother brave. "According to the military attaché I spoke to today, we're not even here." We'd been told the same thing by my Uncle André when he called the embassy to make sure our names weren't on the list of dead and wounded after the American

Embassy explosion in April. They told him they'd never heard of us.

"We don't exist," Etienne said in a sarcastic tone.

The dishes rattled and the living room lit up. We stopped talking as we waited for the boom of the bomb to resound. My father grabbed the wine bottle as it started to topple. My mother reached for the candlesticks while Etienne and I steadied the table.

"One day this whole place will go up in flames," Maman said. "But I won't be here to watch it."

"Lucie," my father said. "You're exaggerating."

"Don't condescend to me." Maman jabbed her piece of lamb with the tip of her knife and cut it into a hundred tiny pieces.

Early Saturday morning, I answered a knock at the door. I'd been perched on the arm of the couch, listening for it for the last fifteen minutes. It was Ginnie and her parents.

"Can you come with us?" Ginnie pressed her palms together in prayer. Her oversized T-shirt had slipped over one shoulder and showed her bathing suit strap.

I ran into the kitchen, where Maman was fiddling with the coffee maker.

"Please," I begged. "Let me go with them. Just this once. She's my best friend, and I'll never see her again after we move." I gave her my most pleading look. I'd managed only one sleepover at Ginnie's house, the month before. But after a car bomb exploded in front of her apartment building on Hamra Street, Maman refused to let me sleep over again.

Maman ran her hand through her hair, adjusted her bathrobe, and stepped out of the kitchen. *"Bonjour,"* she said, and kissed Ginnie's parents on both cheeks while Ginnie and I held our fingers crossed.

Ginnie's mother was tiny, with the same slight build and girlish figure as her daughter. Next to her, Ginnie's father looked like a giant. He wore a faded Boston Red Sox baseball cap, a T-shirt, and jeans. He looked so relaxed standing there — an ordinary American man.

"We'll have her home by tomorrow night," Ginnie's mother said. "The hotel has an outdoor pool with fabulous views of the snowcaps. The fresh air will be wonderful. And it will be good for the girls to get out of the city." She spoke English with a strong Laotian accent.

"Any PLO checkpoints along the way?" my mother asked. We'd been talking about the twelve Palestinian refugee camps along the Lebanese border the night before.

"Nothing to worry about. We'll take good care of her," Ginnie's father said.

"My husband is sleeping." Maman tightened the belt of her bathrobe. "He came home late last night because of roadblocks."

Ginnie's mother nodded sympathetically. "We'll only be a few minutes outside the city."

I put my hands together in prayer like Ginnie was still doing, then ran to my room to grab the bag I'd packed the night before in the hope that our plan would work.

"Don't get kidnapped," Etienne said with a sneer when I passed his room. I could tell he was jealous.

"We'll have her home for supper tomorrow night," Ginnie's father assured my mother. And before she could object, we were out the door and locked into Ginnie's family's compact car.

"We're promoting your general welfare and securing the blessings of liberty," Ginnie said as she squeezed in beside me. It took me a minute to recognize the phrase from the preamble to the constitution. Then I laughed. Maman had said yes! I was on a holiday with Ginnie.

The roads were pocked with craters, and I soon felt carsick. An hour later, when Ginnie's father announced that we'd arrived, it was a relief to stumble out of the cramped car. Ginnie squeezed my hand.

But when we entered our room at the so-called resort, a thick layer of dust coated everything: furniture, bedding, bathroom porcelain. With the door closed and four people inside, it was hard to breathe. Ginnie's mother traced a heart in the dust on the mirror above the chest of drawers. She took a towel out of her bag and spread it on one of the beds. When her husband took his hat off, his balding head was covered in perspiration. All of a sudden, he gave me the creeps. Maybe my father had been right about him.

There was a distant rumble of shelling just then, familiar yet no less haunting than when we heard it in Beirut.

Ginnie unzipped her suitcase. "Let's get in the pool."

The resort was deserted; we were the only people there besides the desk clerk, who spoke only Arabic.

Ginnie skimmed the surface of the pool like an otter. She dove to the bottom and sent her legs up into a perfect headstand, then dropped them down into the splits.

Next to her, I felt like an oaf. I paddled around on my back for a bit, looking up at the overcast sky. I wondered if I could tell Ginnie's parents that I'd changed my mind about coming with them. I was hungry, and regretted having dashed out the door without breakfast. I didn't think I could sleep in our room with so much dust caking the inside of my nose and blocking every pore on my face. And how could Ginnie and I share secrets about the boys at school while her parents lay beside us in the dark?

I wished I'd never come.

I was practising treading water, keeping my head above the surface since I still had my glasses on, when my calf muscle seized up. Searing pain coursed through my leg. I flailed my arms and called for help, but Ginnie and her mom were doing the front crawl side by side, slicing through the water in an elegant race. Her father was nowhere in sight. My leg howled in pain.

"Stretch it," Ginnie's mother said when she finally saw me clinging to the side of the pool and heard my garbled explanation. She reached down and grabbed my leg.

"It's the other one," I gasped.

She flexed my toes and pushed against the sole of my foot. The pain subsided.

"Charley horse," she said, and went back to her laps.

I felt embarrassed and betrayed by my body. I pushed myself up on my forearms and climbed out of the pool, relieved there was no one watching. We'd forgotten to bring towels, and the May air was crisp. I shivered.

"You're getting out already?" Ginnie called from the water.

"I'll just sit here and watch you."

I thought about my family. My father must be awake by now, and angry at my mother for letting me go. What if I got kidnapped and held for ransom like the president of the American University? What if there was a new checkpoint on our way home and our access was denied? All I could think about was going back. I'd never leave Maman and Daddy again. Never beg for another sleepover.

Ginnie's father came running around the corner. "Get out of the pool!" he yelled. "We have to get out of here."

Back at the room, we threw our clothes on over our bathing suits and scrambled to gather our things.

"Get in the car." With his mirrored sunglasses and mean-edged voice, Ginnie's father seemed a different man than the one who'd come to the door in the morning.

"They'll be bombing Jounieh by nightfall," he said once we'd gotten on the road.

"Why didn't they tell you sooner?" Ginnie's mother still had her nose plugs hanging from an elastic band around her neck. Her wet hair was dripping all over the seat and onto her blouse. She pulled it up into a quick bun.

I shivered and sneezed. My T-shirt was wet from the bathing suit underneath and my dripping braids on top.

"Somebody slipped up."

Or we were a target, I thought, remembering my dad's suspicion.

Next to me, Ginnie yawned. "Can we stop for *shawarma* or *shish taouk* on the way home? Swimming makes me hungry."

"First we have to get back to the city in one piece," her dad said. "I can't go very fast on these roads."

I was trying to fit my key into the lock when our apartment door swung open. *"Enfin!"* Maman pulled me to her chest. I could feel her heart thumping through her dress. With my ear next to her body, her voice sounded different, as if coming from inside a deep cave. "We called the hotel, but you'd already left. We were frantic." She released me from her grip. "Your clothes are wet. *Qu'est-ce qui t'est arrivé?*"

Ginnie's mom placed my bag at my feet. "You forgot this in the car."

"Thank you," Maman said stiffly. She didn't invite the family in for a cup of tea.

Ginnie gave me a military salute. "See you Monday. Don't forget to study."

Maman's arm rested heavily on my shoulders. My limbs felt tight and stiff, and a dull pain at the base of my neck extended up the left side of my skull.

Maman closed the door behind Ginnie's family and then sank onto the sofa.

"Do you realize what a close call that was?" she asked. "If you'd lingered a few minutes longer ... That area is now completely closed to civilians ... a combat zone ..."

Home safe. But I had a sudden memory of camping in the Rockies. We could hear a bear grunting through the thin nylon of our tent. "I just want to get warm again," I said through chattering teeth.

In the kitchen, an hour or so later, I pushed a packing box aside to reach the toaster. On the box, under the word *Destination*, *OTTAWA ONTARIO* was scratched out. In its place, my mother had written *SHERBROOKE QUÉBEC*.

"What's this?" I asked. But Maman hadn't followed me into the kitchen. She was still sitting on the sofa, staring blankly as if watching television, except that the set was turned off.

"We're not moving to Ottawa any more?"

"No," she said. "Your father was notified last night, just before leaving the *quartier general*. He's been posted to Sherbrooke, as commanding officer of the recruiting centre."

A fist squeezed my heart. "I thought everything was settled."

"So did we. But the decision is final. No room for negotiation."

After all my father had done in Beirut — shot at twice, MIA, presumed dead — I expected the Canadian government to decorate him with medals, give him a hero's welcome. I wanted Maman to be angry or sad so I could know how to respond. Instead, she just sat there.

"Did Daddy do something wrong?"

She shook her head no.

All these months we'd been talking about Canada like our promised land, where our lives would be peaceful and everyone would be happy. We hadn't yet arrived and already we felt betrayed.

"Is everything going to be in French?" Even though we'd always spoken French at home, my language skills were more limited than they were in English, the language of school and friends, the one I thought and wrote in. "Do you have any friends there?"

"I don't know anyone in Sherbrooke." She looked down at the clasped hands in her lap. "Not a living soul."

LEAVING
BEIRUT

~

Farewell to you and the youth I have spent with you.
It was but yesterday we met in a dream.

KAHLIL GIBRAN
THE PROPHET

I'd been ready to go for the last hour. My suitcase was by the door and my backpack was between my feet. In it was *A Tree Grows in Brooklyn*, my journal, the 1982–83 American Community School yearbook, and a half-written letter to Ginnie that I planned to finish on the plane.

The day before, I'd helped my mother pack the last of our things into boxes. I pictured my favourite novels, *Little Women*, *Tom Sawyer*, and *The Secret Garden*, travelling along a dusty, mine-riddled road between Lebanon and Israel in the back of a United Nations truck in a box labelled *High*

Security, International Documents. I hoped the books would be waiting for me, like trusted friends, when I got to Canada.

"We need to leave in the next few minutes." My father removed his glasses and brought his face closer to the map he'd laid out on the dining room table. He and Ghyslain were debating the safest route to the airport. A bead of sweat slid off my father's nose onto the map.

"There may be surprise roadblocks. It's only nine kilometres, but it could still take us an hour to get there." Ghyslain always spoke as if everything were urgent. In the last seven months, I had rarely seen him without his ear to the military radio. He was obsessed with collecting information and discerning the warring factions' next moves.

"If you forget anything, we'll send it to you." Ghyslain spoke to an area directly in front of him, as if deliberately avoiding any eye contact with my mother or his wife, Violette, who'd come to see us off. "The Avenue de Paris isn't safe any more. They're bombing the hotels and apartment buildings down there, next to the sea. We have to move out ASAP." Ghyslain and Violette were transferring their things into our apartment that afternoon.

"I heard the *Bains Militaires* was destroyed yesterday," Maman said, almost in a whisper. It was the first I'd heard of it. A shiver ran through me, despite the heat. The *Bains* had been my favourite place to go in the city.

I grabbed my backpack and pushed the bulletproof door open one last time. I wanted to move forward, out of there, towards green grass, trees, clean running water, familiar food and language — home.

But no one followed. "Ninety-two days before I go back to Québec," Violette said. My mother gathered her friend into her arms. Resting there, against Maman's capable shoulders, Violette looked like a paper doll, thin and weak, as if her muscles had atrophied over the Lebanese winter. "I can't wait to see my house. And Margot.'

Had she realized she'd named her house before her daughter? I felt sorry for her, but anxious that she not hold us up.

My mother steered Violette toward the couch as if she had forgotten that we had a plane to catch. I let the door swing shut, but kept my back resting against its cushioned layer. My mother's friend had crashed our departure and was claiming all the attention. I'd been counting the days for the last month. I would have liked Maman to slip her arm around my shoulders, part the heavy blackout drapes and stand on my bedroom balcony with me. Together, we could have looked out at the war-torn city. This part of our lives, the military posting overseas, was almost finished. After a few days' holiday in Jerusalem, we'd be home. I wanted her to linger over these last moments with me.

Instead, Violette was hyperventilating. Maman sent me to the kitchen to search for a paper bag. When I came back, the two women were breathing deeply, in unison, and Violette was pulling pictures out of her purse. I leaned in to see the photos, expecting a fat grandbaby drooling for the camera. Instead, I saw appliances.

"The most beautiful kitchen you've ever seen." Violette ran her hand over the photo. "So functional, with lots of cupboards." She blew her nose loudly. "The afternoon sun pours through those west-facing windows."

"Lovely," Maman said, though she was no longer looking at the pictures but at my father, who was pointing at his watch. She nodded in the direction of Etienne's room.

He'd had a particularly bad night, with several bouts of screaming between two and three o'clock. My parents no longer got out of bed to reason with him as they had at first. We all just waited for each crisis to pass. On good nights, the screaming would be over after fifteen minutes. On bad nights, it could take up to an hour before he fell asleep again. We never spoke about his fits, and I grew accustomed to seeing my once ruddy-faced brother with dark circles under his eyes. He was despondent and moody and rarely answered any of my questions about school, the kids in his grade nine class, or the basketball team. He was an impenetrable, brooding presence at the dinner table. Apart from meals, he spent most of his time in his room.

"Time to go," my father said in a no-nonsense voice. Etienne stood behind him, eyes on the carpet. He hadn't bothered to run a comb through his hair, and it looked like he'd slept in his clothes.

I stepped out of the apartment so that I wouldn't have to watch my mother try to separate herself from Violette. Since Sharon, Brad, and the baby had flown back to Canada in early June, along with Doc Miles, who my father had found in Cyprus, the Vaillancourts would be the only Canadians left in Beirut.

Outside, the street was quiet, and there weren't any lights on in the neighbouring apartments. But I had the sensation that our movements were being tracked. I was relieved when everyone came down the stairs and joined me on the pavement. My brother, mother, and I piled into the back seat for our last ride in the Peugeot.

"Pray the airport isn't yet under siege," Ghyslain said.

"And if it is?" Etienne asked. His breath was so rank it stunk up the car.

"*Il faut pas y penser.*" Maman tried to turn around to wave to Violette on the balcony, but she was squeezed in too tightly between Etienne and me.

"What a nightmare," I said, too late to remember Etienne. He flinched and let a deep breath of stale air out of his nose.

Goodbye, Beirut, I said to the buildings and streets as they passed. *I never want to see you again.*

We wove our way through the city, a small white car in a maze of broken streets. From the air, we would have looked like a pinball in an elaborately designed game, forced to change direction every few minutes because of blockades. After about thirty minutes, I saw the air traffic control tower in the distance. "We're almost there!" I shouted. All that was left was to park, check our bags, and get on the plane.

But as we drew closer, soldiers in combat fatigues were everywhere. Feet spread apart in their black army boots, machine guns draped across their chests, they guarded the airport entrance with grim expressions under their green hard-hats.

The tarmac was surrounded by a high metal fence topped with rolls of barbed wire.

My father slowed the car to a crawl. "We may have to take a shortcut to the plane," he said to Ghyslain.

"What do you mean?" I asked, but no one answered. We'd been at this airport only four weeks earlier, when we'd flown to Cyprus for a week's holiday. We'd been dropped off at the door and gone straight to the Swiss Air ticket counter. There'd been a military presence, as there always was in Beirut, but nothing like this.

"I was expecting U.S. Marines," my mother said, "but who are these men? They don't look like the Lebanese Army." When my father didn't answer, she continued in a shaky voice, "Are they PLO? Or Lebanese militia? Maybe we should have tried to leave yesterday. Or during the night."

"You mean we're trapped?" A rush of panic heated my face, while my hands and feet went cold.

"Maybe it was a mistake not to wear my United Nations uniform," my father said.

From the seat behind him, I could see the crease of his perfectly ironed sleeve. I couldn't stop staring at it, unnerved by my father's confusion. He never made mistakes.

"It's too late to change," Ghyslain said.

"It's too late for a lot of things," my mother said.

Two military jeeps came alongside our car. Their drivers stared openly at us but didn't leave their vehicles to ask us who we were. I wished we were in the United Nations jeep my father usually drove instead of our small, inconsequential Peugeot.

My father gave the military drivers each a cursory nod,

as if they were business associates. "Ghyslain will take us through the airport," he said, all hesitancy gone from his voice. "He knows his way around." He spoke as if his friend were taking us on a tour of his neighbourhood.

"What about our luggage?" my mother asked. *"Mes choses?"* The skin on her face was a mottled blotch of red and white spots, and she was craning her neck to see what might be behind our car.

"It will follow," my father said, and stepped out of the car at the same time as Ghyslain. The two men walked up to the airport's main entrance. Ghylsain wore his khaki uniform, with his blue beret folded down over his right eyebrow. My father stood next to him in beige pants and a long-sleeved, pale blue shirt. He did not look like the UNTSO operations officer, but just an ordinary man about to get on a plane with his family. Ghyslain waved at the guards in a friendly way, but they did not wave back.

The men talked with the soldiers guarding the front door, who walked them toward a side door, also guarded. We were clearly not going to saunter up to the ticket counter as we had the previous time.

A Lebanese soldier came over to the driver's side of our car and rapped on the window with the butt of his rifle.

"JésusJosephMarie," my mother said.

Etienne stared at the end of the gun.

"Maman, qu'est-ce qu'on fait?" I asked.

When we didn't move, the soldier said something in Arabic in an angry voice.

My mother reached into her purse and pulled out her

United Nations identity card. She passed it to me since I was sitting behind the front passenger seat, and the guard was nearest to me. "Hold this up to the window." The man didn't even look at the card. Proving our identity as foreign diplomats was not going to help us. He rapped on the window again, harder this time, then went around to the trunk and repeated his Arabic words.

"He wants our bags," my brother said in a flat voice. "Our suitcases."

"Is there a way to open the trunk without getting out of the car?" my mother asked.

By then my father must have overheard the commotion because Ghyslain was striding over to us, waving the car keys in his hand. The men gave our suitcases to the soldiers and indicated for us to remain seated. We watched soldiers and luggage disappear through the airport's side door.

My mother groaned. Since her humiliating body search at the Montreal airport on her first trip to Israel, she was nervous about being separated from her luggage.

I pictured our familiar leather suitcases getting searched and then confiscated or abandoned in the corner of a brightly lit examination room. Like orphans, they would remain behind while we flew off into enemy airspace. Or would we?

If we were taken as hostages, who would lobby for our return? How much would the Canadian government give in exchange for us? My father, surely, would have a certain value. But what about me?

I gripped the backpack on my lap with both hands, like a life vest.

Maman's eyes were glued on my father. He had opened his attaché case and was showing some documents to the two guards. Three other guards, also in full military attire, complete with machine guns, had joined them, forming a circle around my father and Ghyslain.

"We're going to see Jerusalem one last time." My mother unzipped her purse and fingered a thick wad of U.S. bills wedged between a compact case and a travel-sized tissue pack. "The Holy Land. *La Terre Promise.*" She said it softly, as if she were repeating a prayer.

"The enemy," my brother said. My mother didn't answer him.

I had an itchy sensation at the back of my throat. I hadn't had anything to drink since I woke up.

A soldier came through a gate in the barbed wire fence. A black Doberman with a chain attached to its neck trotted at his side, ears pricked forward.

My mouth was unbearably dry. The windows were steaming up, and I was feeling light-headed from the lack of air.

The soldier and the dog walked to the front of the building, where they replaced the guard on duty at the airport entrance. The dog sat on his haunches and looked around. He was like me, taking everything in, assessing the danger. Except that he didn't look afraid.

At last, my father came back to us, escorted by three armed guards. He tried to open my mother's door, but she'd locked it and had to fumble with the mechanism to get it to open. When we finally made our way out of the car, my back was soaked. A small breeze blew against my T-shirt, bringing a cooling sensation. Soldiers looked me up and down as I passed. I could feel their eyes on my wet back. We met Ghyslain at the side door and followed him through.

"We'll take a shortcut through the airport kitchen," Ghyslain said, in a voice that was too loud and cheerful. We walked in single file between the shiny stainless steel counters stacked high with prepackaged airplane food on plastic trays. First in line was an armed guard. Then Ghyslain. Behind him my father. Next came my mother, my brother, and finally me. I wished I had a passport on a string around my neck, tucked under my shirt like my brother and parents. If I disappeared, I didn't have any official identity documents on me except my name printed on a card inside my backpack. No phone number, since our line in Beirut was no longer in use. No forwarding address. No money. I'd given all my *lira* and *piastres* to Ghyslain before we'd left the apartment, after my father had stressed that we must not be in possession of anything Lebanese once we landed in Israel.

I walked quickly, often stepping on my brother's heels as we passed through a corridor of refrigerators, massive, industrial-sized sinks with pyramids of pots waiting to be washed, and cardboard boxes heaped with citrus fruit that gave off a rancid smell.

"Quit it," Etienne snarled.

"I can't help it," I said softly, not wanting to draw attention to myself. I would have hooked my fingers through the belt loops of his jeans if he'd have let me, or held on to his backpack.

We rounded a corner, and I caught sight of my mother's

profile, staring straight ahead, studying the backs of my father's ears with the keen observation of a portrait painter who wanted to memorize every detail of her subject's physique. My father, ever the soldier, walked straight and tall: shoulders back, chin forward, as if it were his typical morning routine to march his wife and children through a foreign airport's kitchen.

I cast a furtive glance at a dark-skinned man in a white chef's uniform. He was chopping onions with the rhythmic precision of a percussionist, his eyes glued to the wooden chopping board. Was he pretending not to see us? Did he know that we were about to board a plane that would fly us from Lebanon to Israel, via Egypt? If he knew, would he call us spies? Blame us for contributing to the mess? Or would he tell us about the loved ones he'd lost in the war, like the greengrocer at the end of our street in West Beirut, who sold my mother his best vegetables because she asked him about his family, all of whom had been killed? One day, he'd pulled a thick bunch of celery from behind his counter and offered it to her as if it were gold. Later that day, when she showed it to us in the apartment kitchen, Maman cradled it in her arms like a baby. In winter, when the borders were closed because of the escalated violence, fresh produce was almost impossible to find. "He had two daughters and a son," my mother said, putting the celery down on the counter and running her fingers along its stalk. "Their house was bombed one morning. He had already left for work. His neighbour two doors down cycled across town, through the rain, to tell him what had happened."

We pushed through the last door and stepped out into the searing heat of the morning sun. It pressed down on my head and radiated up from the black tarmac. A trickle of sweat ran down the inside of my thighs. My eyes stung at the brightness of the light. But there was our Swiss military plane, with its side door open. Our suitcases were waiting for us at the bottom of the stairs.

I was the first to go forward. "Goodbye," Ghyslain said, and wrapped his arms around me. My cheek pressed into his chest. His uniform was stiff and had a sour, sweaty smell like a cup of day-old tea. I was surprised at how tightly he held me, lingering in the hug for a moment before releasing me.

I felt acutely self-conscious, as if everyone were watching this display of affection, so uncharacteristic of our family. I imagined eyes peering out from behind the hundreds of darkened airport windows, watching us take our leave.

"Goodbye," I said, placing my foot on the first step. The metal handrail burned my fingers, but I pressed my weight into it and made my way up into the plane without once looking back.

LET THE CHILD SPEAK

"Now we want to hear all your adventures,
and let us relieve you of your burdens."

JOHANN DAVID WYSS
SWISS FAMILY ROBINSON

In the Arrivals area in Montreal's Mirabel airport, a pair of lovers reunited in a passionate embrace next to the luggage carousel. A fat bouquet of red roses dangled from the man's hand as he lifted the woman off the floor. Nearby, a child ran toward a bearded man in a wrinkly grey suit, arms extended, calling, "Papa! Papa!"

I searched the sea of people holding balloons, flowers and placards, but there was no familiar face, no sign with our name on it.

"I'm back!" I wanted to shout. "We made it!" But the other travellers bustled by, rolling their carts, oblivious to our foursome and where we'd come from.

Maman had explained that her parents' car wasn't big enough to fit all of us and our luggage. It was over an hour's drive from Mirabel to their house, so they'd opted to stay home and let us make our way to Rosemont by taxi. It made sense. But it was a huge letdown.

Outside, I breathed in the northern air — much cooler and clearer than that of the Middle East, without a trace of the spices, roasted coffee, or diesel fumes of Beirut. It was the air of home. And yet not home. Apart from a few months the summer before, I'd never lived in Montreal. I had no attachment to it, no sense of belonging. I folded my jet-lagged body into the middle of the taxi's back seat, sandwiched between Maman and Etienne, just as I had on our drive to the Beirut airport the week before.

Out the window was the city that would be our home until my parents found us a house in Sherbrooke. The trees overwhelmed me with their bushy abundance. I filled my eyes with green. Montreal had no abandoned storefronts riddled with bullet holes. No ramshackle, bombed-out ruins. No refugee camps.

Half an hour into our ride on the Decarie Expressway linking Montreal's West Island to the downtown, a huge boom split the air. Maman screamed. I scrunched down, chest to knees, hands around the back of my head.

After a few moments, Maman's body shifted. I opened my eyes. Above our heads, what was left of the car roof flapped like a parachute. Maman's lips were moving, but I couldn't hear a thing. The noise of the wind ripping through the material was deafening.

Maman leaned over to speak into my ear. "Part of the roof blew off. *Tout est correct.*" She repeated that last phrase as she tried to hold her hair back from her face. Everything's okay.

But it still felt like the sky was falling. The muscles in my neck and shoulders tensed in expectation of an air raid siren. On the other side of me, Etienne pretended to be sleeping, but his eyes moved rapidly under his lids. A blue vein pulsed at his temple.

The damaged roof sagged and then puffed up again. The taxi driver slowed down, but the road was thick with fast-moving traffic, making it difficult to pull over. My father tapped his shoulder and pointed above our heads, but the driver just lifted his palms in a gesture of helplessness.

My mind cycled back to Tripoli, six months earlier: our family following a taxi through an olive orchard at sunset. How I'd wished our car could be like Herbie the Love Bug and fly away, over all the destruction. Back to peaceful Canada. Now we were here, but everything felt wrong.

Grandmaman and Grandpapa were waiting for us outside their brownstone. The first one out of the car, I pressed myself against Grandmaman's soft, round body and stayed there for a long time, wrapped in the floral scent of her face and neck.

My grandparents spoke at the same time. The food on the plane. The length of the flight. The stopover. The war still raging. *Sainte.* The Beirut airport under siege. *Mon Dieu.* The roast chicken in the oven. The pie with strawberries from l'Île d'Orléans. The long-term forecast. The Sherbrooke housing market.

I could have listened to them forever. Their voices were an anchor, settling me into place: their unique brand of French, Grandpapa's colourful Québecois expressions, the small coos Grandmaman made with her throat. They cradled my face, kissed my cheeks, and fondled my braids, said I'd grown into a young woman. Yet Grandmaman called me *belle enfant* and cuddled me like she had when I was small and could fit under her chin.

"We almost sold her for a herd of camels," my father said. It was rapidly becoming a favourite family joke. Although I laughed, it still made me uneasy.

Grandmaman's grip on me tightened. "*C'est vrai?*"

"*Oui,*" my mother said, "*à Damas.*"

Grandmaman cut her eyes at my father as if he was to blame. She turned back to my mother. "You didn't put that in your letters."

"I didn't want to worry you," Maman said, along with a French phrase I couldn't catch.

Grandpapa lifted one of our suitcases up the porch stairs, into the house. "We've been sick with worry. You should never have gone there."

"Never mind." Maman's voice was pinched, as if her shoes were too tight. "We made it out in one piece. It's all just a good story now."

"And what about you, *jeune homme?*" Grandpapa asked as Etienne slipped into the kitchen and made for the guest room we typically shared. "Happy to be back?"

Etienne mumbled his response and flopped onto the twin bed nearest the door.

"Something's wrong," Grandpapa said. "I can tell."

"He's exhausted from the trip," Maman said. "We all are. He'll be more talkative in the morning."

I breathed in the familiar, comforting scent of my grandparents' kitchen, then stepped into the walk-in pantry, my favourite part of their house, and pulled the light fixture's cord dangling from the ceiling. Floor-to-ceiling shelves were stacked with cans, boxes, tins of every sort: all the familiar cereals we'd missed; Nutella; maple cookies; Humpty Dumpty chips; sodas; chocolate-coconut rosebuds. I ran my fingers along the labels, reading their names as if they were old friends.

"I bought you some *crème soda*," Grandmaman said. Her dimpled face beamed.

The cans and boxes blurred. "I missed you," I said, dissolving into sobs.

She gathered me into a tight embrace. "I was scared to watch the news. Thank God you made it out alive."

While my parents went house-hunting and Etienne did a week of summer camp up north, I took a bus to Kanata to visit my old friend Claire.

She squealed when she saw me and threw her arms around my neck. "How was it?" She wasn't a letter writer, and we hadn't talked at all since the summer before.

"Hard." More than anything, I wanted to talk about what I'd witnessed, the war I carried inside. But I didn't know where to start.

I jumped at unexpected sounds in the Savoie's carpeted, air-conditioned house. I was afraid of the dark and didn't want to go out at night.

"I did what you said," I told Claire's mum while we sat together in the spacious living room. We'd come back from the grocery store, where she'd let me pick anything I wanted. "I filled up the journal you gave me."

Mrs. Savoie put down her *Vogue* magazine and patted the huge, purring cat on her lap. "It'll be a book one day."

I thought back to Mrs. Lewis in our makeshift UN school in Tiberias, standing in the rubble of the demolished building. *One day, I'll see your name in print.*

"I want to be a writer," I blurted. Since grade one, I'd dreamed of becoming a teacher. But over the last year, my plans had altered.

Writers were powerful. They could build entire worlds where their readers could escape and become new people. Their power and influence didn't come from weapons and terror. Writers used the most innocent materials that even a small child could wield: pen and paper.

"Keep writing. Don't stop." Mrs. Savoie eyed me closely, as if my face were on the pages of her glossy magazine.

I studied Claire's marmalade cat — an oversized version of Minou — vigorously cleaning its tail. "I've been writing poems." It was true. I had a growing file. But what was also true was that I couldn't write about what I'd seen or heard or experienced over the last year. All those memories were buried in a deep, silent place inside me — a secret chamber like the Well of Souls underneath the cave floor of Jerusalem's Dome of the Rock.

Mrs. Savoie watched me closely for the rest of the week, until it was time for me to take the bus back to Montreal.

"Saying goodbye is part of military life," she said while Claire and I clung to each other one last time. It was something I'd heard my parents say many times. *Incontournable*, my mother called it. Unavoidable.

Claire and I locked eyes. Her father had been posted to Vancouver Island. At the end of the month, she was moving almost five thousand kilometres away. We didn't know it then, but it would be thirty years before we saw each other again.

My parents bought a house — their first in nineteen years of marriage — in a quiet Sherbrooke suburb. There were no blackouts and no bomb threats. We had limitless supplies of both hot and cold water, clean enough to drink right from the tap — luxuries we could only dream about in Beirut. It was what I'd been wanting for an entire year. But I felt hollow inside. I wandered through the house as if lost.

"There's a girl who lives up the street." Maman pointed at the bungalow with the basketball net attached to the garage. But I was too shy to introduce myself, and the girl looked too young to be my friend.

The boxes that had been in storage since Yellowknife now

cluttered up my new room. I opened the one that held my huge pink bear, but it had been packed too tightly. The bear's body was distorted, one plastic eye broken. I stuffed it back in its box. All the momentos from my grade six year — my baton, my Girl Guide uniform with the armful of badges and gold sash I'd worked so hard to earn: how to do the Heimlich manoeuvre, use a compass, read a map, bake a cake, tie a reef knot — made me feel lonely and empty. None of the books I'd kept — my Nancy Drew and Anne of Green Gables collections — appealed to me any longer.

Once all our boxes were unpacked, cousins and relatives came to visit. Everyone wanted to know about the embassy bombing they'd heard about on the news. The talk rapidly turned political as my father explained what the media had gotten wrong or failed to report. This was his story. He was the hero, the one with the mission to accomplish. My stories and Etienne's were merely anecdotal; funny incidents to make others laugh or marvel.

After the relatives were gone, no one asked questions about our year abroad. Even though we were returning from a theatre of war, the Armed Forces offered no psychological support. We were expected to reintegrate into Canadian society and resume our regular daily lives. Apart from the odd phone call from Ghyslain and Violette, or the letters from Brad and Sharon in Richmond Hill with photos of baby Sami, my parents didn't mention our experiences, nor did Etienne.

I rode wide loops around our neighbourhood on my ten-speed, something I hadn't been able to do since leaving

Yellowknife. The speed, the wind in my face, and the freedom I felt on my bike helped to relax the black strap of grief around my chest. I rode as fast and as far as I could until I collapsed, lungs heaving, in our grassy backyard.

In the house, my father retreated to his den, Etienne and I to our bedrooms, and Maman to the kitchen, where she prepared elaborate dishes with all the ingredients she'd missed during our years away from Quebec. She cooked and baked as if she believed every meal could heal us.

Her loneliness was palpable. One day, she said, she would fill the sink with her tears. She wiped her wet cheeks with the dishcloth or the end of her apron.

"*Qu'est-ce que je peux faire pour t'aider?*" Daddy asked her. What can I do to help?

Maman shook her head. "*Rien.*" Nothing.

Etienne and I attended an English regional high school an hour's bus ride away from our French-speaking neighbourhood. Most of the students there — an anglophone minority — had lived in the Eastern Townships all their lives. They all knew each other, whereas my brother and I were misfits; we didn't have the right clothes, expressions, or cultural touchstones. I dreaded finding a place to sit in the cavernous, noisy cafeteria.

Everything about the year before — when I'd leapt out of childhood into the adult world — coiled around me like a venomous snake. But the kids at school weren't interested in talking about the place I'd come from. It must have sounded mythical to them; too preposterous to be true.

School was mostly miserable, with a couple of exceptions: English class, where I excelled, and music class, where I learned to play the piano, an instrument I'd loved all my life.

And then one day, on the long bus ride home, a girl with straight blonde hair and cornflower blue eyes scooched beside me on the narrow seat and started talking. Her name was Anna. She had three brothers who also rode the bus. She was in my grade and wanted to know everything about me. She was kind-hearted and gentle and invited me over to her house.

We adopted each other. Soon we were spending all our free time together. Like Immaculata in Tiberias, Anna had a vibrant love for God and included Him in her merciful view of the world and everything in it, including me.

Having a best friend softened the edges of the anger that swelled up in me — at my parents, my brother, my school, my life. Being angry was easier than being hurt. But with Anna, I could just be silly and smart and thirteen.

She was one of five children in a chaotic household of cluttered surfaces — the opposite of my orderly but silent home. I spent every moment there that I could. When she came over to our place, Anna chatted with my parents as if they were old friends. She loved Coco, my father's new parrot, and enjoyed my mother's fine cuisine.

She sat down to share a meal with us one Sunday evening when my father came to the table holding his portable radio. "A massive bomb destroyed the Marine barracks in Beirut," he said, setting the radio down next to his dinner plate. "And the Drakkar building. The French contingent."

"*Mon Dieu*." The blood drained from my mother's face.

My father fiddled with the radio antenna and turned up the volume. Soon the story was blaring into the kitchen, draping itself over the table like a black shroud. Two suicide bombers had driven their trucks, containing explosives that amounted to twenty-one thousand pounds of TNT, into the Marine barracks and the nine-storey headquarters of the French paratroopers. Over one hundred and fifty U.S. Marines and fifty-eight French paratroopers were dead. They were still pulling bodies from the rubble.

My mind raced to Billy Higgins, my crush in Beirut. His short, stocky frame, his biceps bulging against the sleeves of his combat uniform. The polite way he addressed my mother in his lilting Virginian accent. "Will they list the names of those who died?"

My father, transfixed by the BBC broadcast, hushed me. The Red Cross had found the body of an elderly Lebanese man, identified as Habib Far'awn, the Marines' custodian. "Mr. Habib," my father said. "He used to sleep in his concession stand next to the barracks so he could watch over all the comings and goings. We all bought our cigarettes from him. Always the best price we could find."

Tears fell onto Anna's empty plate. She got up and gave my father a hug, then made her way around the table to Maman, who was still standing with her hands in her red oven mitts. Anna hugged me and then Etienne, who shrugged her off.

"It's just like the embassy." Etienne pushed his chair away from the table and grabbed his skateboard next to the door.

My mother dished *coq au vin* onto my plate.

"Reagan wants all Americans to leave," my father said. "He wants them out by Christmas."

A cresting wave began in my chest — a rush of sorrow at all those Marines who would not be going back to their families. Fathers and brothers and sons who hadn't escaped in time.

"Maybe they shouldn't have gone in the first place," Maman said.

"Maybe none of us should have gone," I said.

My father did not disagree.

The next week, the international peacekeeping force withdrew from Lebanon, where they'd been stationed since the 1982 Israeli invasion. We never heard if Billy Higgins had been counted among the dead.

A few years later, my father received the Order of Military Merit, a promotion to lieutenant colonel, and the long-awaited posting to Ottawa. But by then my brother was about to enter his last year of high school, and I was in grade ten. Since our return to Canada, my parents had often discussed various possibilities for their retirement. According to the terms of his contract, my father would have to retire from the forces by the age of forty-nine. Sherbrooke was not part of his retirement dream.

My parents talked about the potential move to Ottawa late into the night while I lay in bed, unable to sleep. I couldn't bear the thought of moving away from Anna. Starting over. By then, I'd switched to a French semi-private girls' school, mastering my complicated cradle language at last. I wanted to stay in the Eastern Townships forever.

Next morning, at breakfast, Maman announced their decision. "We're staying," she said. "It's final. We want you to finish your schooling in Quebec." Etienne and I had had enough change, she said. It was only fair.

My brother graduated from high school and left for military college in St. Jean, to study science and play college football. The next summer, when I was sixteen, my father retired from the Forces. He and my mother looked into buying a ten-bedroom Victorian house in a nearby village. They'd run it as a bed and breakfast. I asked my parents if I could tag along on their visit to tour the house and meet its owner.

Mrs. Price was a tiny, grey-haired lady with a severe curvature of the spine. She sat us down around her antique kitchen table and served us endless cups of tea. "I want to know who I'm selling to," she said.

My father talked about his career, all the places he'd served. Mrs. Price asked many questions. When it came to the year we'd spent in the Middle East, she turned her rheumy eyes on me. "What was it like for you, tagging along?"

"She's resilient," my father said. "We taught our children to be flexible." He launched into an explanation of the American school my brother and I had attended in Beirut, but Mrs. Price cut him off mid-sentence.

"Let the child speak."

I blinked back at her.

"What was it like for you?" she asked me in a gentle tone. "I'd like to hear your story."

I squirmed in my seat. It was the first time an adult had asked me that in front of my parents. Israel and Lebanon — the war, the peacekeeping mission — had always been my father's story, not mine. It felt strange to do the talking instead of him. I bumbled my way through an answer, feeling intensely self-conscious.

My parents didn't end up buying the Victorian house. Instead, they moved to a mountain village an hour's drive away.

Many years went by. But Mrs. Price's words never left me. *Let the child speak.*

~

CARRYING
WAR

~

After lunch at my parents' house, Etienne and I go for a walk. It's a grey day, with sleet that freezes when it hits our jackets. We're forced to walk slowly on the dirt road, careful not to slip on the ice hidden under the thin layer of snow.

"I can't believe I spent twenty years in Ottawa," he says, kicking at a rock, "when I could have been exploring the world, like we did as kids. I'm finally an expat again."

"We're so different," I say.

I set down roots at the first opportunity. When I first met Brian, my husband, it was his geography that drew me to him: a true Quebecer, born in Sherbrooke like his parents and grandparents before him. We built a lakeside house in North Hatley, a ten-minute canoe ride from the cottage where

Brian spent his summers. We've raised our four children here.

"I want my kids to see the world," my brother says. "I planned to take the family to Dubai for Christmas, but with this isis business, we cancelled and came here instead. My company gives us two free flights back to Canada each year. So, as long as we fly through Montreal, we're covered." He knows how to keep the conversation pleasant. He is winsome, with a generous smile.

"Do you like your job in Paris?" Talking about work feels like a safe topic. It's been so long since he left home; we barely know each other anymore and he asks few questions about my rural life or my teaching and writing career.

"Our offices have moved. Real estate is expensive, so we've gone to an open concept in a brownstone in the *cinquième arrondissement*." He grimaces. "I miss having my own office."

"What do you actually do?" All I know is that he works in communications for a multinational company. The wind picks up again, and I pull my tuque down to cover my ears.

My brother pauses, looks up into the trees. Maybe he's spotted a snowy owl or a pileated woodpecker. I listen for the telltale sound of beak on wood.

"I'm negotiating an arms deal."

"What?" I'm sure I didn't hear him right.

"France is selling to Lebanon. They're sophisticated weapons — missiles and rockets. For the Lebanese Army."

I hear my brother's screams cutting through the darkness in our Beirut apartment. I see his ashen face, the way he closed in on himself after the American Embassy was bombed.

"Couldn't you switch departments?" I study my feet.

"Why? I don't have any problem with it. My company sells to developing countries. There's nothing wrong with defending your people."

"What if the arms end up going to terrorists?" I take my mittened hands out of my pockets. In case of a fall, my hands will soften the impact.

He doesn't answer my question. "With my background in the Armed Forces, the defence department is what I'm most qualified for."

I think of the stories he's told me about the years he worked as a correspondent for the United Nations in the former Yugoslavia, during the war. How he'd counted dead bodies in a gymnasium in Visoko, a few hours southeast of Sarajevo. Since it was the village's biggest building, the UN used it as a makeshift morgue. They'd pulled the bodies out of a mass grave as part of their investigation into war crimes.

A cameraman, newly arrived from Canada, had been assigned to follow Etienne around in an effort to document the UN's involvement in the war. The stench of the rotting bodies was so strong that the cameraman couldn't hold the equipment. He had to cover his nose to block the smell. Every few minutes, he turned away to retch.

He pointed to the half-eaten sandwich in my brother's hand. "How can you stand there and eat?"

It was then, Etienne had told me, that he knew he needed to get out of there. He'd grown numb to the pain; lost all his senses. It was the only way he could survive.

He came back to Canada, got married, and started a

family. In spite of recurring knee and hip injuries resulting from his shorter leg, he ran marathons and did Ironman competitions, purging the memories from his body with each gruelling race.

We're nearly back at my house. I can smell the wood-smoke in the air. Brian must have made a fire with the logs from the apple tree we were forced to cut down two summers ago, after it caught a disease that caused it to rot. I still hate to look at the stump and remember the glorious tree that once stood in its place.

The snow has turned to a hard rain. When I get inside, I put the kettle on. Set my hat and mitts by the fire to dry. See what the kids are up to.

The evening news announces a terrorist attack on a Paris metro station.

"*Mon Dieu.*" My mother covers her face with her hands.

"Not my part of the city," my brother reassures her. "I'm safe, Maman. Don't worry."

The next day, he gives me a hug before leaving for the airport. His family is already in the car. He points to his carry-on bag on the floor next to the door. *Best Canadian Essays* is sticking out of the front pocket. "I stayed up late last night, reading your piece about the bombing. I'm going to read it again on the plane."

I feel a rush of relief. Pull him into another hug. There's no knowing when we'll see each other again. We're worlds apart, and yet there will always be this invisible cord — a double helix of sibling experiences — that connects us. "It was all such a long time ago," I say. "We're different people now."

"Yes and no," he says.

I know what he means. For all these years, we've carried these memories inside us like grenades.

Maman striking a pose in downtown Beirut.

Author's Note

I began writing this story a few days after 9/11. The U.S. had declared its War on Terror — a multidimensional military campaign that included major wars in Afghanistan and Iraq, exorbitant military spending, and an effort to counter anti-Americanism in the Middle East. The world around me was teetering violently on the edge of a precipice. Memories surfaced and refused to be pushed back down. I started writing in my twelve-year-old voice, letting the child within me speak about the profound and far-reaching effects of war.

I wrote in a compressed, lyrical way, looking sideways at the trauma rather than full in the face. It was the only way I could do it. The memories were vivid, as if they had just happened. My experimental essay, titled "The Twelfth Year," went on to be nominated for a National Magazine Award in the "One of a Kind" category — an unexpected success for an emerging writer.

I thought I'd gotten it out of my system. But several years later, on the morning of September 16, 2013, the story grabbed me by the throat once again and refused to let go.

I was at my village library, attending a meeting of my local writers' group. The workshop leader gave us the first prompt: to write about a political event with an emotional impact. My mind went blank. I hadn't listened to the news in weeks. But I put pen to paper and wrote the first thing that came to mind.

At the end of twenty minutes, as is our custom, we read our writing aloud to the group. When it was my turn, I read the first few sentences, and then my voice caught, and I couldn't go on. Thirty years had passed since the event I had written about, but it still ravaged me. The other writers were quiet witnesses to my struggle. When I was finally able to read, they listened avidly. Afterwards, they were full of questions.

I'd written about the massacre of Sabra and Shatila, where thousands of undocumented men, women, and children were brutally murdered over a period of three days, their lifeless bodies picked up by a bulldozer and thrown into mass graves.

Once the workshop was finished and I returned home, I wasn't sure if I'd remembered the event or the place correctly. I googled Sabra and Shatila, unsure of the spelling. What I saw on the screen gutted me. That day, September 16, 2013, was the thirtieth anniversary of the massacre. Not only had I remembered, I'd gotten each detail correct. Right down to the date. The article confirmed what my parents had told me back in 1983 when we'd visited the camp: no one took responsibility for the terrorist act that decimated an entire community. There was no retribution. The international community turned a blind eye.

I couldn't get the coincidence out of my mind. I didn't know what it meant, but I knew I was called to give account of what I had seen, heard, felt, and carried within me still. I was called to be a witness.

I'm grateful to my parents and brother for their enthusiastic and gracious response to the many essays I've published on this subject over the last eighteen years. *Peacekeeper's Daughter* is extrapolated from those essays. I've set the story down the way I remember it and filled in the blanks where my memory flagged, particularly in the area of dialogue. I've changed the names of the characters, but they are all based on real people. To simplify and streamline, some characters are composites of more than one person. While some scenes are composites of real incidents, all the events related in the book are factual. Wherever possible, I cross-referenced specific historical events such as shootings, bombings, assassination attempts, and massacres with numerous internet resources and news reports, as well as long discussions with my parents. However, this is not a journalistic work; it is based on one person's experience, filtered through memory and interpretation.

In the time it took me to complete this book, my four children have grown from infants to adults. Our world has undergone vast changes. But Beirut continues to be the capital of local, regional, and international terrorism — in need, more than ever, of peace.

Recommended Further Reading

Abirached, Zeina. *A Game for Swallows: To Die, to Leave, to Return*. New York: Graphic Universe, 2007.

Abirached, Zeina. *I Remember Beirut*. New York: Graphic Universe, 2014.

Al Rabeeah, Abu Bakr and Winnie Yeung. *Homes: A Refugee Story*. Calgary: Freehand Books, 2018.

Chai, Ang Swee. *From Beirut to Jerusalem*. Kuala Lumpur: The Other Press, 2015.

Dan, Uri. *Ariel Sharon: An Intimate Portrait*. London: St. Martin's Press, 2007.

Friedman, Thomas L. *From Beirut to Jerusalem*. London: Picador, 2012.

Khalidy, Soraya. *Le goût de Beyrouth*. Paris: Mercure de France, 2003.

Makdisi, Jean Said. *Beirut Fragments: A War Memoir*. New York: Persea Books, 2007.

Shadid, Anthony. *House of Stone: A Memoir of Home, Family and a Lost Middle East*. Boston: Houghton Mifflin Harcourt, 2012.

Acknowledgements

Thank you to my parents, who now live next door to me, near the lake, where we all plan to stay for the rest of our days.

Thank you to my wonderful husband, Brian, and my four children: Jacob, Emma, Micah, and Priscilla, who've been my biggest fans.

Thank you to my beloved friend, fellow writer, and critique partner Michelle Barker for reading and editing countless manuscript drafts and encouraging me through every step of the process. Michelle, I could not have done it without you.

Thanks to my Eastern Townships writers' group: Brenda Hartwell, Nancy Branch, Kathleen McHale, Ellen Goldfinch, Mead Baldwin, Susan Macaulay, Marjorie Bruhmuller, Jackie Hyman, Barbara Elliot, and especially Carolyn Rowell and her husband David Baldwin for reading early drafts.

Thanks to fellow writers Connie Braun, Lesley Finn, and Tara Westover for giving insightful and thoughtful feedback on the manuscript.

Thanks also to Brian Henry, Trevor Corkum, Hilary McMahon, Barbara Berson, Wayne Grady, and my fellow MFA students at UBC, who read bits and pieces and gave insight and writing wisdom, particularly the members of the

Raspberry Cordial Collective: Michelle Barker, Tara Gilboy, Kate Lum, and Patti Edgar.

Heartfelt thanks to Elizabeth Philips and Caroline Walker at Thistledown Press, for championing this manuscript. Your 'yes' has made all the difference. Thank you for the amazing team you put together: Naomi K. Lewis, my editor, Roberta Coulter, my copyeditor and Nathaniel Moore, my publicist.

Mille mercis, mon amie Line Fortin, for proofreading all the French snippets.

Several of the chapters in *Peacekeeper's Daughter* were published in Canadian literary journals. Huge thanks to *Grain* literary journal and editor Rilla Friesen for publishing "The Twelfth Year," an early version of the book in essay form, and nominating it for a National Magazine Award and a Western Magazine Award. This was deeply encouraging to me. Thank you to *Event Magazine* for publishing "Beirut Bombing," and to Christopher Doda and David Layton for selecting it for *Best Canadian Essays 2015*, published by Tightrope Books.

Thanks to my treasured friend Mary Hill, for buying an entire box of books and giving them to everyone for Christmas. Everyone needs a friend like you.

Thanks also to *Prairie Fire* for publishing "Witness," and to *Malahat Review* for publishing "Terrorist Narratives," which draws from some of the material that appears in the book. I'm especially grateful to Emily Donaldson at Biblioasis Press, who selected "Terrorist Narratives" for *Best Canadian Essays 2019*, and to *The New Quarterly* for selecting "Terrorist Mythologies," a follow-up to *Peacekeeper's Daughter*, as the runner-up for the 2020 Edna Staebler Personal Essay Prize and publishing it in their Fall 2020 issue. Thank you to *subTerrain* for publishing my essay "Carrying War," which won second place in the Lush Triumphant Literary Awards for nonfiction in 2019.

Thank you also to the Canada Council for the Arts for awarding me a grant, and for helping me to believe that I had an important story to tell.

Gratias maximas vobis ago.

Born in Germany to French-Canadian parents, Tanya Bellehumeur-Allatt grew up on various army bases across Canada, from Quebec's North Shore to Yellowknife, Northwest Territories. When she was twelve years old, her family moved to Tiberius, Israel, where her father served as a United Nations peacekeeper on the Golan Heights. When war broke out with Lebanon, Tanya and her family moved to Beirut, where they lived for seven months, at the height of the Lebanese civil war. Tanya's journal from 1982–1983 became the seeds of her memoir, *Peacekeeper's Daughter*. Tanya holds an MA in English Literature from McGill University and an MFA in Creative Writing from UBC. She lives in Quebec's Eastern Townships with her husband and four children. Find out more about Tanya and her writing, including her debut poetry collection, *Chaos Theories of Goodness* (Shoreline Press, 2021) at https://tanyaallattbellehumeur.com.